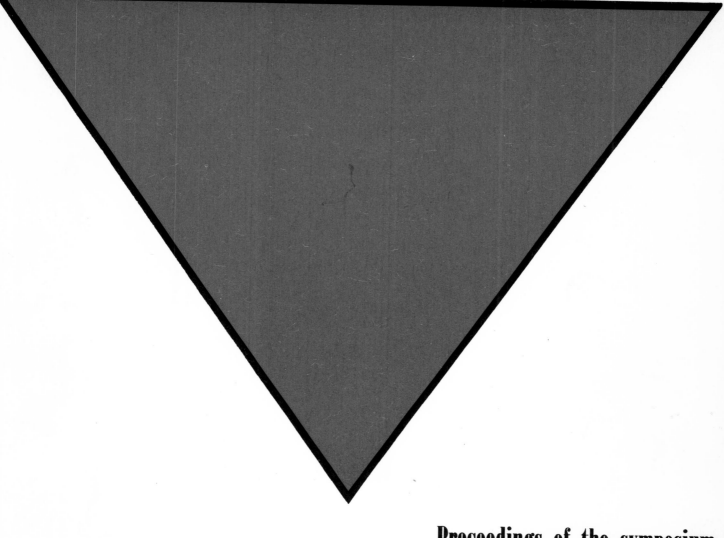

Proceedings of the symposium
POPULATION GROWTH:
CRISIS AND CHALLENGE
January 9 & 10, 1970

COLLEGE OF HUMAN BIOLOGY
The University of Wisconsin-Green Bay

uwgb
YEAR
ONE

$1.50

Population Growth: Crisis and Challenge

9, 10 January 1970
Green Bay, Wisconsin

Sponsored by

COLLEGE OF HUMAN BIOLOGY

The University of Wisconsin – Green Bay

Edited by

John R. Beaton
Alexander R. Doberenz

i

1970 Proceedings of the First Population Symposium
at The University of Wisconsin – Green Bay

Second Printing – December, 1970
Third Printing – June, 1971

Library of Congress Catalog Card Number 70-630651

Printed in the United States of America

ii

C O V E R

The red triangle on the cover of these Proceedings represents the Family Planning symbol of India.

A C K N O W L E D G E M E N T

The partial support of this Symposium by Eli Lilly and Company is gratefully acknowledged.

P R O C E E D I N G S

Additional copies of these Proceedings may be purchased by writing to:

COLLEGE OF HUMAN BIOLOGY
The University of Wisconsin - Green Bay
Green Bay, Wisconsin

Checks should be made payable to
The University of Wisconsin - Green Bay (CHB)

P R E F A C E

This Symposium on "Population Growth: Crisis and Challenge" was first conceived in the late summer of 1969 as a fitting way in which to embark upon the first year of operation of the College of Human Biology in the new University of Wisconsin - Green Bay, which is committed to ecology - man and his environment.

The greatest single problem facing manking is the rapid population growth. This Symposium, as reproduced in this text, considered the many consequences of the explosion along with possible means of regulation. It is the hope of the Planning Committee that this will not be just another Symposium where much was discussed and then was soon forgotten. Rather, we hope that an awareness has been created and will be maintained, and, most important, that positive action will be taken now - while time, albeit limited, is still available.

Irene B. Taeuber
Alexander R. Doberenz
John R. Beaton

January 1970

T A B L E   O F   C O N T E N T S

CONTRIBUTORS

Dr. Dean E. Abrahamson	Department of Anatomy and Department of Laboratory Medicine University of Minnesota, Minneapolis
Dr. John R. Beaton	College of Human Biology University of Wisconsin - Green Bay
Dr. Frank Byrne	Secretary of the Faculty University of Wisconsin - Green Bay
Dr. Jerry W. Combs, Jr.	National Institute of Child Health and Human Development Bethesda, Maryland
Dr. Alexander R. Doberenz	College of Human Biology University of Wisconsin - Green Bay
Miss Sharon A. Estel	Student University of Wisconsin - Green Bay
Dr. Jeremy Green	Webster Clinic Green Bay, Wisconsin
Mr. David H. Greenwood	Student University of Wisconsin - Green Bay
Dr. Paul Gyorgy	Department of Pediatrics University of Pennsylvania School of Medicine and Philadelphia General Hospital
Dr. Ruth E. Hartley	College of Human Biology University of Wisconsin - Green Bay
Dr. William C. Kaufman	College of Human Biology University of Wisconsin - Green Bay
Mr. Robert T. McLaughlin	Office of Population Ford Foundation New York, New York
Dr. Ronald J. Pion	Department of Obstetrics and Gynecology University of Washington Seattle
Dr. Edward H. Storey	College of Creative Communication University of Wisconsin - Green Bay
Dr. Irene B. Taeuber	Office of Population Research Princeton University Princeton, New Jersey
Dr. Edward W. Weidner	Chancellor University of Wisconsin - Green Bay

ix

NOTES ON THE SPEAKERS

Dr. Dean E. Abrahamson received the M.A. degree in physics from the University of Nebraska, the Ph.D. degree in anatomy, and, in the same year, the M.D. degree from the University of Minnesota. He holds membership in 10 scientific societies, and, most appropriate to this Conference, is president of the board of the Minnesota Committee for Environmental Information.

Dr. Jerry W. Combs, Jr. is Chief of the Behavioral Sciences Branch of the Center for Population Research in the National Institute of Child Health and Human Development. Dr. Combs has a Ph.D. degree in Sociology from Columbia University. From 1951 to 1953 he was on the faculty of the Department of Sociology at Emory University in Atlanta, Georgia, where he taught Population, The Family, and other courses in Sociology. From 1953 to 1957, he was with the Air Force Personnel and Training Research Laboratory engaged in manpower research, and from 1957 to 1969, when he joined the Center for Population Research, was Chief of the European Branch, Foreign Demographic Analysis Division. U.S. Bureau of the Census.

Dr. Paul Gyorgy holds the M.D. degree from The University of Budapest and an honorary Doctor of Medicine degree from the University of Heidelberg. He holds membership in 19 scientific societies and has been recipient of a number of national and international awards including the Borden Award (twice), Modern Medicine Award of Distinction, Goldberger Award of the American Medical Association, Osborne-Mendel Award of the American Institute of Nutrition, the Mickle Fellowship of the University of Toronto, and the Howland Award of the American Pediatric Society. Perhaps best known for his discovery of the vitamins riboflavin, vitamin B6 and biotin, Dr. Gyorgy is author or co-author of several books and monographs and over 400 scientific and clinical publications.

Robert T. McLaughlin holds the B.A. degree from Harvard College and the M.P.A. in Public and International Affairs from the Woodrow Wilson School of Princeton University. Following extensive experience with the U.S. Peace Corps in Peru and with A.I.D., U.S. State Department, Bogota, Colombia, Mr. McLaughlin joined the Office of Population, Ford Foundation in 1968.

Dr. Ronald J. Pion holds the M.D. degree from New York Medical College with post-graduate study and specialization in obstetrics and gynecology at UCLA and at the Karolina Sjukhuset Hormon Laboratoriet in Stockholm, Sweden. Recipient of a number of scholastic awards, Dr. Pion is a member of eight scientific societies in the areas of obstetrics and gynecology and of endocrinology. He is active in a number of community organizations concerned with family planning and sex education, and is a member of the Population Crisis Committee (Washington, D.C.) and of the American Association of Planned Parenthood Physicians (New York). He is author or co-author of 26 scientific publications.

Dr. E. H. Storey received his M.A. and Ph.D. degrees from the University of Illinois, where he subsequently served in the Department of Recreation and Park Administration in addition to holding an appointment as Professor of Urban Planning. Dr. Storey has developed park and recreation plans for some 20 cities for which he served as consultant in planning park resources and developing leisure services. He is author of numerous professional publications. Among several society affiliations, Dr. Storey is past president of the Illinois Park and Recreation Society and served as chairman of the Research Committee, American Recreation Society, and as director of the Society of Park and Recreation Educators. He joined the University of Wisconsin - Green Bay in August, 1968.

Dr. Irene B. Taeuber holds the Ph.D. degree in sociology from the University of Minnesota, the LL.D. from Smith College, and the D.Sc. from Western College for Women. A member of a number of scientific societies, Dr. Taeuber is past president of the Population Association of America, vice president of the International Union for the Scientific Study of Population, Fellow of the American Association for the Advancement of Science, and member of American Statistical Association, Pacific Science Association and American Sociological Association. She is author or co-author of some 10 books and over 200 articles. Her major current research interest is the population of the Chinese cultural area.

MORNING SESSION

9 January

Chairman - Dr. John R. Beaton
Dean, College of Human Biology
University of Wisconsin - Green Bay

Introduction and Welcome

John R. Beaton

On behalf of the University of Wisconsin – Green Bay, and specifically the College of Human Biology, I extend a sincere welcome to our speakers, our panel members, and to each of you present here today. This is the first major conference sponsored by the College of Human Biology in its first year of full operation; considering the qualifications of the participants who have agreed to be with us, I feel certain that the Symposium will attain its goals. Perhaps I should take a few minutes in this introduction to review briefly our goals and format.

First, let me say that a major role of a university is to meet the needs of its community; the University of Wisconsin – Green Bay takes this role seriously. However, as we travel through Northeast Wisconsin, impressions of open space and the absence of serious overpopulation are acquired. Why then a Symposium in Green Bay on the problems of the population explosion? One answer is that Northeast Wisconsin is in the fortunate position of being able to prepare for the development of overpopulation here, and to benefit from the experience of other overpopulated areas. To ignore the problem elsewhere and to say that "it can't happen here" is foolish and to take the attitude of the ostrich with its head in the sand. We cannot afford to do this. Already, certain aspects of the problem are with us; these will be compounded as our population grows and other problems will be added.

Basically, environmental pollution is a result of population; there is no question that we have pollution problems now. High costs and taxes - particularly in relation to education - are with us. Land costs soar as demand for buildings and space increase. We can see this happening now in Green Bay. Costs of food increase as availability decreases. In Brown County, the number of persons employed in agriculture is diminishing; this is reflected in rising urban values and decreasing rural values. Perhaps more important, this indicates a trend toward decreased agricultural potential. Overcrowding itself is associated with many serious sociological and psychological problems.

3

These are evident in any large city in the United States and in core areas of smaller cities. Unfortunately, although much is known of the effects of overpopulation, there is inadequate understanding of effective prevention or alleviation. I might say that because we understand this reasonably well demonstrates poor acceptance of the methods. It is a major goal of this Symposium to consider both the effects of overpopulation and its prevention. You will note from the program that today we are concerned primarily with effects and tomorrow with prevention. At the end of each day's session - today and tomorrow - there is a panel discussion. I want to emphasize that at these Panel sessions, questions or comments from the audience are not only welcomed, they are encouraged. We hope this will be more of a forum than a panel discussion.

Allow me to return for a moment to the population situation in this area. I will use Brown County as my example. I have stated already that there appears to be no serious overpopulation here at present. However, let's look at a few facts and figures.

From 1940 - 1950 population growth rate in Brown County was 1.83% per year. From 1950 - 1960, this increased to 2.7%. An annual growth rate of 2.7% may seem small. However, present world growth is about 2.1% per year - less than that of Brown County. At present rates, it is estimated that the population of the World will double in about 35 years; that of the United States, depending upon the figures you use, from 50 to perhaps 65 years; and that of Brown County will double in about 25 years. Thus, 25 years from now, if it is unchecked, the population here will be double what it is today. The annual growth rate in India, a country recognized as seriously overpopulated, is about 2.5% - less than that of Brown County. There is another interesting facet to the local situation: most of the increased growth that we have seen in the past decade at least is in two distinct age groups - those under 16 years, and those over 65. This demonstrates, if you like, an increased birth rate and the well-known decreased death rate. Fortunately, there is some evidence of a recent small decrease in the birth rate in Brown County; but this small birth rate decrease may be more than compensated for by migration into this area. The nature of the population is changing, the age group is changing, and this requires planning for the future. Recent history and the future forecast demonstrate that our apportionment of time to work and to leisure is changing - this is changing across the nation. Greater demands are being placed upon recreation and leisure facilities, particularly those concerned with water. Yet, as we will hear from Dr. Storey later today, these facilities are rapidly diminishing, both in number and in areas for several reasons.

I realize that I may have painted a pessimistic picture, but this does not exclude possibilities for optimism if we plan and prepare now to take action and just don't talk about it. At least partial solutions have been applied in other countries under conditions much more difficult than in the United States. We have learned a great deal from the experience of others and it remains now to apply this knowledge to our own situation. We hope that this Symposium will serve to consider both the problems and the possible solutions, and, from the standpoint of our College, to provide a basis for the implementation of a meaningful program of Population Dynamics.

Introduction of Dr. Irene B. Taeuber
John R. Beaton

It is with distinct pleasure that I introduce Dr. Irene Taeuber as keynote speaker of this Symposium.

I would be remiss if I did not acknowledge Dr. Taeuber's assistance and advice in designing and developing our meetings today and tomorrow. When we first considered the need for a Symposium on the Population Crisis and were seeking a keynote speaker, the name of Irene Taeuber was suggested by a number of sources.

If you will examine Dr. Taeuber's summary shown in the program, I think the reasons for our choice will be obvious. She holds senior teaching and research positions at both Johns Hopkins University and Princeton University and is author of some 10 books and over 200 published articles. It was most fortunate for us that Dr. Taeuber could take time from a very busy schedule to be here and we are most grateful to her. It may be of interest to the group here that Dr. Taeuber will leave later this month for two months in India, followed by a month in Singapore, Hong Kong, Taiwan and Korea working in the field of population research. This is certainly not her first trip to the Asian countries.

This morning, Dr. Taeuber will speak to us on the topic "Population Outlook in Asia", based in large part upon her extensive experience and writings in this area.

Population Outlook in Asia

IRENE B. TAEUBER, Ph.D.

Senior Research Demographer
Office of Population Research
Princeton University

In the 60's, there were massive increases in the populations of the less developed countries. There were spreading recognitions of the critical hazards of overly rapid population growth to economic development and to human welfare. In some countries, there were quickening speeds and deepending intensities in the many types of action essential to economic and social development and demographic transformation. In others, there was lethargy, inaction, or, more seriously, limited achievement from plans and actions. Birth control programs had stimulated declines in birth rates that were already declining - but there was no unassailable evidence that they had initiated decline in any major country.

The preceding comments were prosaic and complex. They were stated deliberately in prosaic form. This is a research conference and the dissections that underlie research, as research itself, are analytical rather than crusading activities. They were complex because the striking statements that are so tempting are likely to be imprecise. One of the derivations from the analysis of the changes and stabilities, the developments and non-developments, of the 60's is the knowledge that problems associated with population growth, as growth itself, are variable in origin and historic evolution. Futures are not predictable either narrowly or broadly, whether in the short or the long run.

An insistence on unpredictability may seem incongruous as an approach to the demographic dimensions of the future. Perhaps it is. It may be quite unrealistic, though, to pose a dichotomy of highly effective population programs and precipitant drops in birth rates on the one hand, the cataclysmic dooms of famine, disease and disorder on the other. The dichotomy may be appropriate to some areas but not to others. Or there may be a middle way between millenium and catastrophe. Or science, technology, and the ingenuity of man may alter dimensions and directions in the future, as they have in the past.

These statements risk interpretation as the irrelevances of academia in a world requiring action - immediate, direct, and as gigantic in scope as the magnitude of the problem with which it deals. They are intended as preface to five arguments:

1. The decade of the 70's, as that of the 60's, will be one of severe demographic difficulty in much of the less developed world. Unless intensive, extensive, and appropriately directed activities designed to reduce rates of population growth are taken within the next decade, the problems of population growth will approach the insoluble in many areas in the last decades of this century and the early decades of the next.

2. The knowledge essential to the design and implementation of programs and the guidance and integration of developments in the many fields that influence population status and change does not now exist, or exists only in its approximate beginnings. Research that is directive, imaginative, and incisive rather than pedantic and repetitive is required as basis for the knowledge that underlies policies, programs, activities and achievements.

3. The present and the prospective future relations between population, development, social order, and political stability differ among the cultures and the countries. Hypotheses of diversity underlie the argument that priorities in research should be accorded the separable and associated relations of population with location, culture, color, social order, and political form in historic generation and present status.

4. The futures of populations and of problems associated therewith may involve the widely ramified interrelations of developed and developing countries. There are great regions where inter-penetrations may be predominant over separateness, whether in cooperation, precarious balance, or conflict.

5. Population projections usually assume continuity in levels or persistence in trends from past to future. In recent decades, the record of projections as predictions has been notably poor, whether for developed or less developed countries. The records of Japan and the United States are glaring illustrations of the inability to predict fertility. The swift declines in mortality that transformed the slowly evolving problems of population growth in the less developed areas to the present crisis of swift growth were predicted neither by demographers nor by bio-statisticians.

If these arguments and statements are even approximately acceptable, there is an obvious conclusion. Neither the folk wisdom, the judgments of men of good will, the historic experiences, the sciences and technologies, nor the policies and the plans of the 60's are sufficient for the 70's and the decades thereafter. The requirements in demographic and related research extend from new or modified concepts and hypotheses to reanalyses of existing and incoming data and the design of new studies. The requirements in biological, chemical, and bio-medical research are immense. The ramifications extend to all sciences concerned with earth, man, and the interrelations of the two.

The broad frame of populations facts and research queries across space and time is not an introduction to a discussion of all topics. It is, rather, preface to a different focus on specific demographic developments and outlooks through taking a long view of a wide region. The geographic area is Asia - from the Arctic to the Indian Ocean, from the Ural Mountains to the Aleutian Islands. The time span is the next century. Contrasts of Asia in 1870 and in 1970 demonstrate the wisdom of the long view as a base for alternative hypotheses and the allocation of research priorities among them.

The research approach to the demography and the development of Asian peoples and cultures over the next century requires escape from the present convention of separating developed and less developed countries, and then assessing separate futures. Asia includes Eastern Siberia and the Soviet Far East. This northern part of the continent is highly developed; there are major resources along with sparsities of people. The Asian peoples below the Soviet frontier are generally less developed. Here is the world's largest agglomeration of the unskilled, the poorly educated, the hungry, and the frustrated. Developed resources are limited and people are many. Then there is Japan - a century ago peripheral even among the less developed areas, now in the forefront of the developed areas. If research is to encompass the developments that influence economies, societies, and populations, the analysis of the Asian past and future must include northern America. The Eastern Pacific is counterpart to the Western Pacific. The directions and the dimensions of the Asian future involve the interrelations of the world's most numerous peoples, those of the Indo-Pakistan subcontinent and China, and the three largest industrial nations, the United States, the U.S.S.R. and Japan.

A few figures on the size and the potential growth of the world's less developed peoples suggest the numerical dominance and the research priorities of the Asian populations. The estimated population of the world is now 3.6 billion. If birth rates remained constant, 3.9 billion more people would inhabit the world at the end of the next three decades. In the year 2000, the world's population would be 7.5 billion. The population of the less developed countries is now 2.5 billion. With unchanging birth rates, numbers would increase 3.4 billion to reach 5.9 billion in the year 2000. Almost 87% of the increase in the world's population in the last 30 years of this century occurs in the less developed countries.

Asian populations dominate both the present numbers and the annual increments in the populations of the less developed countries. In 1970, more than 1.9 billion of the world's 2.5 billion less developed peoples were Asian. If birth rates remained unchanged until the end of the century, 4.5 billion of the world's 5.9 billion less developed people would be Asian. Asians would constitute more than half the increase in population for the world as a whole, more than three-fourths that for the less developed countries.

Some 1.9 billion Asians in 1970, almost 4.5 billion Asians in 2000 - will not the pressures of the increasing numbers and the recognition of the still greater numbers to be expected in future years stimulate whatever types and intensities of activities may be necessary to slow the growth? If the natural correlates of economic and social development, transfers of people from rural to urban areas, and programs to diffuse birth control practices should result in declines of birth rates to half their present levels by 2000, would not the massive increases of numbers be averted, the problems avoided? A cautious answer based on an assessment of past and present experiences in Asian countries has to be negative. Changes in birth rates that now seem achievable can slow but not eliminate growth within this century. Assuming the reduction of birth rates to half their present levels by 2000, Asia's less developed population would increase from 1.9 billion in 1970 to 3.3 billion in 2000. The increase of the three decades would be 1.4 billion. In other words, a reduction of birth rates to half the 1970 levels by 2000 would yield populations in 2000 three-fourths again as large as those in 1970.

The fact that slow and sustained reductions in birth rates that would halve them within 30 years does not eliminate growth, does not mean that such reductions would not lessen the problems of development. By the end of the period, all age groups below 30 would be increasing less rapidly than they would have been without the reductions in birth rates. The relative burdens of dependent children and youth on adults in the productive ages would be less. Moreover, the achieved declines prior to 2000, the age structures less favorable to growth, and the continuing declines in birth rates after 2000 would make the problems of population growth more manageable in the early decades of the next century. The operational difficulty is major, though. The present rates of growth are heritage of the past. The reductions in rates of growth achieved in one generation alleviate the problems of growth somewhat for that generation, but the major contribution is to future generations. Hence that which may be postponed as not the most urgent of present problems may assume an increasing urgency over time.

The increase of the populations of the less developed Asian countries from the 1.9 billion of 1970 to the 3.3 or 4.5 billion of the end of the century is difficult to evaluate as probability or to assess in terms of correlates and consequences. The projected increases will not become realities if there is economic deterioration and political disintegration. Increases in the numbers of people that amount to billions do not occur in the absence of economic and social developments and political stability. People do not live without food, shelter, clothing, and minimal sanitary and health facilities. What we are saying is that there are paths to the future quite different from those that are now projected as one form or another of ordered continuity from past through present to future. The growth rates of the present era were produced by declines in death rates. The respite from the levels of human wastage that characterized past eras may be temporary. Death rates could move upward again. Increases in mortality could come slowly with malnutrition, declining vitality, and lessened controls of environment. Or there could be famines, epidemics, flights, and major deteriorations in man-land relations. Or the disintegrations of local orders and national political instabilities could destroy the precarious balances of production and consumption that now exist in the monsoon lands of Asia.

10

Description, analysis, and assessment of an Asian present and an Asian future, involve over-generalization, even if limited to the less developed areas. The programs and activities to sustain the increasing populations, the policies and programs to reduce birth rates, and the avoidance of disintegration and cataclysm remain basic responsibilities of the nations. The directions of development or retrogression and hence the proper paths for research are national and regional rather than continental. The major demographic divides in Asia are those between the peoples of the Indo-Pakistan subcontinent and Southeast Asia on the one hand, the Chinese and the related peoples of East Asia on the other.

The deepest demographic crisis is that in Middle South and Southeast Asia. The focal center is Middle South Asia. The population was 422 million in 1940 and 747 million in 1970. There was a 77% increase in total numbers in these thirty years. If declines in birth rates begin now and rates are halved in the next thirty years, population will increase 650 million to reach 1.4 billion in 2000.

These broad numbers are so staggering in their implications as to require restatement. The population of Middle South Asia was less than half a billion in 1940. It was three-quarters of a billion in 1970. If birth rates are halved while death rates continue downward, it will approach one and one-half billion at the end of the century.

Is this projected future a feasible one? The answer is that we do not know. The maintenance of the increasing numbers requires economic and social development. This development that is essential to declining birth rates also yields declining death rates. Continuity in backwardness is not compatible with continuity in growth in Middle South Asia. The question of the future of population is the question of the future of comprehensive modernization.

Can India and Pakistan achieve rates of economic and social development to sustain the growing populations at rising levels of living? Can there be the increasing capabilities and aspirations among the people that are basic both to economic growth and to social change? Will there be postponements in marriages, smaller families, more equalitarian roles for the sexes and the generations, and advancing opportunities for children? The answers involve imponderables as to the uses of presently known sciences and technologies and unknowns as to the sciences of the future. The newer agricultural techniques and associated infra-structures could result in very major increases in food production. Theses of the inevitability of famine have lost their plausibilities, but the possibilities of mounting insufficiencies of food and eventual famines remain. The probabilities of achieving rapid declines in birth rates are inseparable from the probabilities of achieving effective development programs.

The great questions of the future of the populations of the Indo-Pakistan Subcontinent have no precedents in history. There is far too little that is directly relevant in social, psychological, political and cultural research. The descriptions of aroused expectations among the peoples in the 50's and the early 60's were apt, but the expectations were seldom met. Today transistor radios in remote regions permit unity in concensus or in rebellion prior to the literacy and the transportation and communication networks once believed essential. Neither the potential leadership nor the volatility of the frustrations among the people are yet known. There are deep diversities in culture, religion, language, personality orientations and life styles, as in physical features and ethnic origins. There will also be deepening forces of unrest unless the nations can provide employment and meaningful lives for the maturing youth who cannot be absorbed productively in agriculture, who have no frontiers internally or externally to which to move, and who are economically and socially marginal in the cities to which they are migrating.

Many of the immediate problems of the 70's seem insurmountable on any assumptions that now seem realistic. This is particularly true of the lower Ganges-Bramaputna area, the home of the Bengalis, whether in East Pakistan or in India's West Bengal.

If the question is not the decade ahead but the year 2070, our tasks in the outline of the future of Middle South and Southeast Asia may be likened to those of the economists who assessed the futures of economies and populations on the eve of the Industrial Revolution and the great demographic transitions among European peoples without glimpsing the imminence of either. It may also be that the penalty of two centuries of partial Western penetrations with population growth but without modernization is the inability of the hundreds of millions who now exist to move directly to modernization.

The divide between the worlds of Middle South and South East Asia and East Asia in Singapore, where a largely Chinese population in a tropical city state is characterized by a very high rate of economic growth and a rapidly declining fertility. The northern anchor of this East Asian Chinese cultural region is Japan, where a Chinese-based people and culture have moved within a century from ancient feudalism to become the world's third industrial power, from premodern balances of high death rates and _mabiki_ - controlled birth rates to rates of reproduction insufficient for replacement. Between, on the mainland, is the world's largest cohesive ethnic group and its least known population outside some of the tribal societies, the Chinese.

There is not the time here, nor would the distraction be justified, to summarize the state of knowledge and ignorance on the historic growth, the present state, or the future prospects of the population of China. In the estimates and medium projections of the United Nations, the population of Mainland East Asia is 532 million in 1940, 718 million in 1970, and over one billion in 2000. Increases are two-fifths in the first and again in the second thirty-year period. The slower rate of growth than that in South Central and South East Asia is due primarily to assumptions of lower premodern birth rates, an earlier initiation of decline, and hence a more advanced state of transition in 1970 and an earlier completion of transition.

The true enigma in Asian and in world population is not the precise figures on the numbers, the distribution, and the dynamics of the Chinese population that demographers would so like to have. It is, rather, the questions of the ability of this oldest and ablest of the world's still traditional cultures to achieve a unity that is tuned to science and the future rather than to ideology and archaic technologies. The answers to the Chinese future do not lie in demography, but no analysis of the Chinese, the Asian, or the world future can neglect either the present numerical primacy of the Chinese or their distinctive potentialities for demographic modernization.

Birth rates are now low or declining in all the Chinese and related populations of the China perimeter. As we noted earlier, Japan's birth rates are below permanent replacement levels. Her problems are those of labor scarcity, declining school populations, metropolitan proliferation, and rural depopulation. The traditionally high fertility of the Koreans is declining. Fertility in the Ryukyu Islands is as low as that in the adjacent prefectures of Japan. Fertility has been declining in Taiwan since the mid-fifties. It is declining in Hong Kong and Singapore and among the Chinese of Malaya. In all these areas, there are high rates of economic growth and major strivings for ever higher educational levels. Ages at marriage are advancing and families are increasingly modern rather than traditional in orientations and aspirations. The processes of modernization in the Peoples Republic of China have involved all the classic problems of demographic transition.

The dynamics of population in the first two decades of communism involved direct movement from premodern balances of births and deaths without a long colonial interlude of unchanging fertility and slowly declining mortality. The declines in death rates must have been swift indeed as internal order, more evenly distributed food, and driving campaigns for sanitation and disease control replaced the deteriorating conditions of the century of disintegration and deterioration, disorder and conflict, internal and international war. There may have been temporary increases in birth rates. Peace and the establishment of order were conducive to reunited families and new marriages. Crusades for the equality of women and against the selective elimination of girl babies should have contributed further to growth. The large cohorts of the births in the early 50's replaced the depleted cohorts of the 40's and earlier years. Swiftly declining hazards permitted increasing proportions of those born to survive.

The impact of population growth on the economy and the social order of China was delayed by its localization in the oncoming cohorts. The increasingly large age groups began to reach school ages in the mid-50's . They began to reach the years of labor force participation in the middle and late 60's. It is enticing to speculate on the relations of the dynamics of the increasing cohorts to the Red Guards and the later forced movements to the countryside and the frontiers.

The ideology and the ideals of the Peoples Republic are alike conducive to reduced birth rates. The emphasis on loyalty and service to state rather than to family, the ideal of equality for women, the advancing legal age for marriage, and the shattering of local insulations should all be conducive to smaller sizes of families in the long run. As early as 1956, the health services stated that contraception, sterilization, and induced abortion would be available. By 1964, the equipment for suction-type induced abortion was being produced in China. The selective survival that we can infanticide was one of the pragmatic adaptations in traditional Chinese culture. There was no religious, ethical, moral or customary repudiation of induced abortion as somehow differentiated from contraception.

There is widespread concensus among students of China that birth rates have been reduced in the urban population. The great questions concern the rural sector that is predominant in the population. Knowledge is limited severely. However, analyses of the interrelations of industrialization, urbanization, and social change in areas of record in pre-communist China suggest processes similar to those that underly the past demographic transition in Japan and to those that now underlie the transitions in Chinese populations on the perimeter of the mainland. This is not an argument substantiating the fact of declining fertility in the communes of the more advanced regions of the Peoples Republic. It is an argument in support of the hypothesis that declines are now, or will soon be, in process in great areas of China.

There is another argument for the plausibility of ongoing or imminent transition in China. All those below age 21 were born under the new regime. Young adults in their twenties have only childhood memories, if indeed there are memories, of the tragic and chaotic decade of the 40's. Women conditioned to the old China are now in their middle or late childbearing years. The critical decisions as to limitations of births are being made by young families whose major conditioning occurred under communism. Within a decade, the critical decisions will be those of youth born and reared under communism.

The assessment of the demographic future of China involves the speed, the types, and the extent of the comprehensive modernization. The history of the last century involved the disintegration of the Ch'ing Empire, the struggle for reintegration, and its final achievement under the Peoples Republic. In this century of China's failures, the Japanese made the complete transition from ancient to modern in economy, use of human resources, and vital balances. The Russians occupied their present areas from the Urals to the Pacific. The goal and major achievement of Imperial Japan was the economic development and the industrialization of China's northeastern provinces. It was in Chinese areas that a Japanese defeat of the armed forces of Imperial Russia marked the beginning of a new era in world history. The economic relations and the political conflicts of China with the U.S.S.R. and Japan need not be retold here.

14

There is no alternative to advanced economic development if the future of China is to remain Chinese. Is there, then, a future in advanced industrial development such as they already achieved by those countries of the Northern Pacific that bound or surround China?

The timing of the Chinese transformation in the late 20th and early 21st centuries makes transition to industrial status and demographic balance feasible in theory. The advances in types and techniques of food production provide the time essential to the modernization of family and fertility. The pragmatism of the Chinese and the closeness of models enhance the probabilities that the timing of increasing food production and declining fertility may avert true crises in growth.

Modern science and technologies are transforming the definitions of resources in the northern Pacific region, including China.

The assessment of the future of the population of China thus merges into that of the developing world industrial region in the Northern Pacific. The context is far removed from that of demographic doom. The historical demographers of 2070 will analyze the developments and the interrelations of Pacific populations across the century that is then past. It is possible that a modernized and educated Chinese population will be a major asset of China and the Pacific region, just as the modernized and educated Japanese population of 1970 is a major asset not only to Japan but to a vast Chinese cultural area moving in modernization.

NOTES ON SOURCES:
The estimated and projected populations of countries, regions, and the world are taken from the estimates of the Population Division of the United Nations. See: United Nations. Department of Economic and Social Affairs. World Population Prospects as Assessed in 1963. Population Studies No. 41. New York, 1966. vii, 149 pp. Preliminary and summary projections for a more recent period were presented to the last meeting of the Population Commission. There are no major differences that would alter any of the analyses presented in this paper.

The analyses of the Chinese populations are derived from an ongoing study of the Chinese population. A more elaborate discussion of the Pacific as a region and the diversities within it was presented in a paper to the Pacific Science Congress in Tokyo in 1966: "New Dimensions in Pacific Demography". The proceedings of the symposium in which the paper was included are being published in Japan early in 1970.

15

Discussion - Dr. Taeuber

DR. BEATON:

We were going to withhold questions after each of our talks today until the panel this afternoon, at which time all of the speakers will be appearing. However, we do have about 5 or 10 minutes before we take a coffee break and I am wondering if any of you would like to ask Dr. Taeuber a question while the thoughts are fresh in your mind.

Q. A point of clarification - did you say that birth rates could be separated from the general economic development of a country, such as possibly death rates?

DR. TAEUBER:

I said they could not be. There is increasing evidence of interrelations. In the Chinese populations of the China perimeter, In Korea, in Japan, and in the United States, the closest of the social associations of marriage, family and fertility, are those with education. Education itself is an indicator variable; it is a measure of modernization. In the countries of the Western Pacific when birth rates were declining prior to intensive family planning programs, the acceptance, the practice, and the efficiency of birth control went upward across a modernization continuum. Now, there is some evidence in Taiwan that birth control programs may be able to reach couples prior to modernization. No country has yet achieved low birth rates prior to modernization. But the use of the past to predict the future is hazardous.

Thirty years ago the population of the United States was believed to be facing decline. The official projections around 1940 were that the maximum population of the United States would be 160 million and that it would be reached by 1960 or soon thereafter. Our numbers would now be declining. A bill was introduced into the Congress to have family allowances in order to raise the American birth rate. But the birth rate did not continue on its expected downward trend. Rather, it increased sharply. By the year 1957 it reached the rate of 25 per 1000 population, far less than half that in Colonial days, but sufficient to give very substantial growth. We demographers had a lot of fun computing when the population of the United States would reach one billion. More seriously, official projections carried these numbers up and up. Again we became concerned about population trends after they had shifted. Our birth rate has been going down since 1957; the crude birth rate in 1968 was the lowest in American history. There is a point in this long digression. What we know about the critical interrelations between population and other trends is limited. The real questions concern the interrelations that will exist when science, technologies, political conditions, and free decisions of nations differ from those that now exist.

17

The greatest priorities in research involve the forms of motivation and the institutional changes that lead to the acceptance of family limitation prior to the achievement of universal education, non-agricultural employment, and adequate levels of income. The future of the Indo-Pakistan sub-continent and the future of much of Latin America and Africa may depend upon the answer to that question.

Q. I want to ask Dr. Taeuber - does she mean by birth rates and fertility?

DR. TAEUBER:

No. There is always a bit of difficulty in simple discussion. The term "birth rate" is easily understood. This is simply the number of births per thousand to the population. Now, the changes in the birth rate reflect temporary factors in the age distributions of the women, what happened to marriage rate the year before, etc. The changes in birth rates may reflect either short run changes or long run trends.

If we are looking at the trends of population, the major interest lies in the reproductive history of generations of couples who move through the child bearing ages. We need more refined measures of reproduction than simply the relation of annual numbers of births to total population. In this paper, the term "fertility" was used to indicate inherent levels or changes.

Q. How do you measure fertility?

DR. TAEUBER:

One of the measures of fertility from census statistics is the number of children ever born to women age 45 to 49, i.e. those who have completed their childbearing. This is a measure of the reproduction of a generation. Another measure is the gross reproduction rate. This is a hypothetical figure. It is the number of girl babies born to 1,000 women, all of whom survived from birth to the end of the child bearing years, and bore children at each age at the same rates as the women in the particular year and groups of comparison. There are many other measures of fertility, but these are indicative.

Q. Are there any statistics available pertaining to the population of China?

DR. TAEUBER:

There are many statistics and there are wide variations. This is not a simple world in which we live. Statistics vary widely by countries. China was not colonial; one of the penalties is that there was no colonial census. In the Indian sub-continent, the British took a census each 10 years from 1881 to 1941, while India and Pakistan took censuses thereafter. What we do have for China are many figures that come from the Chinese registration system. We have censuses for areas of China; these were collected in the main by Japanese who ruled Chinese areas, or by the British in Hong Kong or Singapore. There were Chinese groups who engaged in statistical activities in China. Thus it is extremely difficult to answer questions for all China. There are data for the Japanese and Korean populations and for Chinese populations under alien rule. Within China, postponement of marriage was widespread. There was a fair proportion of men who never married. Except in exceptional areas of favorable living conditions, Chinese fertility was not extremely high. There are few Chinese groups that had fertility as high as that of today's populations in East Pakistan or the Phillipines. Fertility was limited by the percentages of men who never married, the postponements of marriage among men who could not afford to marry, by practices of selective survival, and by taboos against child bearing in the later ages.

DR. BEATON:

If my figures are correct, we hear a great deal about Japan having essentially, but not completely, solved its problem of overpopulation. Obviously, they had to because Japan is restricted to islands; land is certainly at a premium. Japan, I think, is about 70% mountainous, not available for agriculture, for example, or living space. Now, if I am correct that Japan has essentially solved the problem, or did a few years ago, I wonder if Dr. Taeuber would like to comment on not exactly how they did it, but how could they do it successfully in Japan where many other countries have tried almost the same procedures and have not met with the success. Is this the motivation of which we spoke?

DR. TAEUBER:

The people of Japan solved the population problem of Japan, the government came tagging along behind them. There was no official population program in Japan except to spread contraception to eliminate the harm of induced abortions. The government issued a white paper approving the diffusion of contraceptive practice, but by the time they issued the paper, the birth rate was already below 18.

Japan's demographic and economic modernization occupied a century. Japan was already developing commercially when an imperial council decided to open the country to Admiral Perry rather than to the Russians. There was comprehensive and guided modernization, beginning with the Meiji restoration of 1868. There has been more than a century of a modern type urban industrial development in Japan. In the early 1870's for instance, Japan provided for universal education, compulsory and equal for girls and boys.

The population changes prior to the Pacific War were classic in their simplicity. Death rates went down; there is substantial evidence that birth rates were already moving downward by about 1885. By the late '30's, a year or so before the Pacific War, the birth rate was below 30. It was lower than the birth rate in Taiwan now. In fact, the only driving population policy that Japan ever had was adopted in 1940. Its goal was to raise the birth rate in order to produce enough Japanese to fulfill the imperial destiny in the co-prosperity sphere. It was not a program to decrease the birth rate. The Pacific War came; at the end of that war most of the cities of Japan were in ruins. There were seven million men under arms; there were separated families and postponed marriages. There was severe malnutrition, but little starvation. In late 1945, '46 and '47, something like five million Japanese were repatriated to Japan. People began to move back into the cities; families were reunited; marriages occurred. There was a major baby boom. The birth rate rose to 36. This was when we became excited about Japan's population increase.

In the meantime, the Japanese were concerned about a variety of things. One was eugenic, the undue increase of the "unfit". Legally, there was nothing medical people could do about women who came back pregnant from what had been the co-prosperity sphere. In 1949, the Japanese passed a re-vision of a eugenic protection law that had existed in pre-war time. This law provided for contraception, sterilization, and induced abortion, in the health centers or outside, under carefully controlled conditions, for a long list of "hereditary" deficiencies, most of which weren't hereditary. It also provided for these anti-natalist services for mothers whose lives would be threatened by various and sundry medical causes if they had another child. Then, economic causes were included. Nobody discussed this inci-dental inclusion of permissive induced abortion. The excitement in the passing of this law was that it put contraception in the health services.

But two years after the law was passed, the number of women visiting the health centers requesting service was negligible. Few Japanese women would go up and move through a door that said "birth control". But in Japan there is no ethical distinction between contraception and abortion. Further-more, Japan has a major supply of unemployed medical people. All of the doctors who had been in the imperial area or service in the 7 million armed forces found themselves returned to the area of birth in Japan, without jobs. It is in this setting that the phenomenal increases in induced abortion occurred. Abortion was in the private sector. It was not a policy of the government of Japan.

The government provided training courses for doctors, and only desig-nated physicians who had had this medical training were permitted to do in-duced abortion. This was a health measure. When the Diet of Japan became concerned with the increasing problem of induced abortion, they would appoint a committee to make recommendations with reference to the eugenics protection law. The committees that they appointed would be selected from the associa-tion of obstetricians and gynecologists, and they would recommend further liberalization of the laws. By 1952 abortions could be performed by decision of the individual doctor. Whether this is a government policy or not may be debated. But the government of Japan did not define a problem of excessive population. It did not adopt measures to reduce the rate of population growth.

20

Introduction of Dr. Paul Gyorgy
John R. Beaton

In introducing our next speaker, Dr. Paul Gyorgy, I would like to reflect for a moment upon an incident of about 20 years ago. As a new graduate student, I was presenting my first scientific paper at an international meeting - a paper which dealt with some preliminary research on Vitamin B_6. Naturally, I was very nervous in this new role. However, after my presentation, a senior scientist in the audience took time to compliment me on my work and to set my mind fully at ease. It wasn't until later that day that I learned this gentleman was Dr. Paul Gyorgy, who had first discovered and described the Vitamin B_6 which I was studying. I believe this incident exemplifies the interest of Dr. Gyorgy in all people as individuals and particularly as students. It is an incident which I have not forgotten. Since that time, I have met with Dr. Gyorgy on a number of occasions - most notably at a symposium on Vitamin B_6 held in his honor in New York; researchers, clinicians and teachers from around the world participated in honoring this scientist and friend.

To list Paul Gyorgy's many accomplishments, honors and positions would take all morning and time does not allow for this. Let me just say that he comes to us with a vast background of experience and knowledge in nutrition and related fields, and, most importantly, with the proven desire to apply these to the betterment of man. I can think of no person better qualified than Paul Gyorgy to speak on the topic "Malnutrition is a Problem of Ecology".

Malnutrition is a Problem of Ecology

PAUL GYORGY, M.D.

Professor Emeritus of Pediatrics
University of Pennsylvania
Active Consultant,
Philadelphia General Hospital

The gap between the affluent few and the hungry millions in developing countries and that between the many affluent and relatively few, but still, considerable number of poor in highly developed countries is widening and may become unbridgeable if properly directed efforts are not put into effect without delay.

In the great majority of developing countries today, 70 percent (or more) of the children under 6 years of age are malnourished and have no opportunity of developing their full potential. Malnutrition may start with the foetus in utero. In the United States the number of malnourished individuals is estimated to be about 15 million. The group of pregnant and nursing mothers, infants and of pre-school children, up to 6 years of age, represents the most vulnerable age classes and are especially difficult to reach. Early malnutrition may have a lasting imprint on the physical and mental development of infants and young children. Their physical growth and final maturation of many of their organs, to name only two - the brain and kidneys - shows the relatively greatest speed (after fetal life) in the first 3 - 5 years after birth. The limits of irretrievability of damage resulting from early malnutrition and other injurious environmental factors, such as broken home life, have not yet been fully defined. However, it is highly probable that without improved nutritional and social conditions the damage of early childhood may engulf the corresponding generation leaving its mark on the general social, economic and cultural development of the nation, developing countries as well as those disadvantaged groups in highly developed countries.

As in the fight against infectious diseases, prevention of malnutrion is vastly more important than treatment. This approach in the control of malnutrition has not yet received in the past or even in recent years, the emphasis it merits. Preventive measures should apply to pregnant and nursing mothers, as well as to infants and young children.

In the recent White House Conference on "Food, Nutrition and Health, held in Washington, December 2 - 4, consensus was noted on the elimination of "hunger" and as sure remedies were recommended by the majority of those in attendance: "The flow of dollars and food (Food Stamps)". In this symposium being arranged by the new College of Human Biology, an especially desirable and praiseworthy innovation in our academic life, it is essential to take issue with the above mentioned points of view.

1. "Hunger" may be an attractive political slogan but has no true scientific connotation to the overriding problem of nutrition (malnutrition) or even to health. Admittedly, any normal human being becomes hungry if food is missing for a more or less prolonged period of time. However, hunger is a psychological sensation and as such has to be differentiated from the physical-nutritional fact of true starvation. As a matter of fact, prolonged hunger without available food ends, especially in adults, in loss of appetite, or of hungry sensation. Ravenous hunger, with food within reach is often found in obese people, who as such are "malnourished" but are certainly not starving.

2. Neither the flow of dollars nor that of food (stamps) alone will with certainty lead to the improvement of nutrition or of health. Millions of tons of milk powder was sent in the past 25 years to developing countries, without any reliable information of success.

Increased income will not necessarily guarantee improved "housekeeping" with its attributes of better nutrition and health.

Modern psychology stresses more and more the importance of learning through "conditioning" for behavioral changes. "Education" with its traditional lectures, posters, slides, radio or movies is not replacement for conditioning through direct and persistent personal contact. Infrequent short visits of families to health centers and out-patient clinics, or vice versa, of health personnel or nutritionists and home economists to the home are no substitutes for continuous contacts.

Malnutrition is by no means a health problem alone. Especially in its preventive aspects, there should be a joint effort in applying the principles of ecology which includes all environmental factors, such as public health, agriculture, economics, education, demography, cultural anthropology, psychology and social welfare. This synthesis has not been carried out to any appreciable extent in the past.

In order to avoid any misunderstanding it should be pointed out that the word ecology originates from the Greek "ecos" which means home, house. Thus, not only the total, wide environment, as recently being stressed in connection with pollution, conservation, etc. For the human eco system, home and family remain the center.

Previous attempts to cover at the outset the entire country or even large segments of it were irrational and doomed to failure.

In the total ecological approach, one should first start with relatively small demonstration projects, which would permit continuous surveillance, base line and repeated evaluation studies. No proper evaluation over an extended period of time was ever conducted in the past.

One should think of such projects in the United States - (1) in a city ghetto; (2) Chicano communities in Texas; and (3) in Appallachian areas in Kentucky or Tennessee, with a population of about 10,000 - 20,000 in each project.

The program should be approved by the local (state, county, city) government and be placed preferably under the direct supervision of neighboring health services.

It is obvious that improvement of ecology involves not only health or disease but many other sub-sections of health including family planning, social welfare and also many other branches of the local government, such as education, agricultural extension, community development, economy, poverty programs, etc. Past efforts suffered from fragmentation, instead of the desirable unified direction. Even concentration on Health Delivery Systems misses - as amply demonstrated in the past - the adequate and persistent human element.

In this respect, a very important - even essential - role should be assigned to young "volunteers" (male and female) without any special expert training, generalists. In their selection special attention should be paid to their individual motivation, humanitarian qualities, idealism and a high degree of unselfish compassion.

The volunteers (college graduates, students, even high school graduates) should be required to reside in the communities for an extended period of time (1 - 2 years duration). It is important to place volunteers into the communities of the same cultural and ethnic background. Naturally members of VISTA with experience should also be considered.

The training of volunteers for their activity in the communities should be relatively short (6 - 8 weeks) and multipurpose in nature, including methods of evaluation of changes. They should follow the program plan under the surveillance and direct supervision of the local health authorities. Special expert consultants should be made avaiable as well as local experts in education (including nutrition), community development, family planning, social welfare, agriculture, etc. The selection of Health Services as the direct supervisory agency is explained by the prominent part physical and mental development of infants and young children should occupy in the evaluation of results obtained.

The volunteers should make friends with the inhabitants of the community through single visits to the houses as well as in group meetings. They should prepare folders for each family, covering all aspects of the ecology. Observations made in the family should be currently entered into the folders. In yearly intervals evaluation in all phases of progress should be an essential part of the observations.

Proper change of behavior and attitude should be attempted not by coercion but with empathy, as a kind of group therapy where the group consists of the inhabitants and the "teacher/missionary" represented primarily by the resident volunteers. Disadvantaged people anywhere in the world crave for love, understanding and humanity.

It is desirable that the volunteers recruit acceptable and adaptable helpers from the community who can assist them in various activities, such as establishing care centers, promoting breast feeding, family planning and where feasible, poultry raising, home gardens, etc.

In the line of the major topic of this Symposium, i.e. Population Growth: Crisis and Challenge, the role of local helpers, such as older, respected ladies of the community, is of particular importance. They could act as the best and probably most acceptable promoters of family planning, much better than by cursory outside "expert" visitors.

The United States is the 16th nation with their yearly infant mortality figure (24%). Among several possible ecological factors, the almost complete disappearance of breast feeding must be named as certainly a very important one. Here again, younger and older married women of the community could be utilized as proper catalysts. The Childbirth Education Association and La Leche League succeed in larger cities in a truly remarkable way in the promotion of natural childbirth and breast feeding. They are entirely volunteers, using personal contact and group therapy as their approach.

If and when smaller well-controlled demonstration projects prove the feasibility and desirability of this avenue, one could and perhaps should make a big step forward: a general draft for young men and women to serve 1 - 2 years in the interest of their country. Proper selection, adequate training of these volunteers are just as important as for the initial demonstration studies.

Your new College of Human Biology is ideally set up to live up to your original idea and become a true "Focus on Ecology". The common denominator remains "Humanity". This should evoke a special echo in the youth of today. In paraphrasing a statement written by Kenneth T. Young, former U.S. Ambassador in Thailand and now President of the Asia Society, ". . . it seems to be increasingly recognized that the essence of challenge to understanding and coping with the problem - - - of general rural and urban rehabilitation is human" (1).

In conclusion, one could also quote the South Vietnamese Buddhist monk, Thich Hanh: "Problems come if you live too comfortable a life and sufferings arise. When you focus on yourself, you find many more problems. Not realizing the suffering around you in the world - I don't think it is a happiness. You feel loneliness and emptiness, and these are more unbearable than any other kind of suffering. . .The most effective medicine is an experience of the suffering around you. Then you heal." (2)

References:
1. Asia 6:6, 1966
2. New Yorker, June 25, p. 21, 1966

GENERAL READING SOURCES

Gyorgy, P. and O. L. Kline, Eds., Malnutrition is a Problem of Ecology, S. Karger, Basel (Switzerland) 1970

Gyorgy, Paul and Anne Burgess, Eds., Protecting the Pre-School Child, Tavistock Publications (1965)

Nutrition Research in Indonesia and Thailand, Special Issue, The American Journal of Clinical Nutrition, Volume 20, Number 12, Dec. 1967.

Introduction of Dr. E. H. Storey
John R. Beaton

At this time, I wish to introduce our next speaker, Dr. Ted Storey, Dean of the College of Creative Communication of the University of Wisconsin - Green Bay. Although we can point to Ted Storey as one of our own group, it should be noted that this training and experience in leisure sciences antecedes by some years his joining our University.

A Canadian by citizenship, Dr. Storey received his formal graduate training at the University of Illinois where he held teaching, research and consulting positions before coming to Green Bay in 1968.

Today, Dr. Storey will sepak to us on the topic "The Leisure Explosion" - a problem area which has not yet received adequate consideration in relation to the population growth. Dr. Storey speaks from a broad base of experience and from a concern with the population explosion.

The Leisure Explosion

Edward H. Storey, Ph.D.

Dean, College of Creative Communication
Professor of Leisure Sciences
University of Wisconsin-Green Bay

In a human society that places more importance on reaching the moon and leap-frogging to other planets than it does upon improving the human condition, it may seem an exercise in futility to exert concern about the problems and opportunities of leisure. It is difficult for many to regard leisure as a problem. Even if one limits his concerns to the welfare of the earthbound, it may seem difficult for us to take seriously a phenomenon that most people seem to regard as being rather pleasantly at the fringe of life.

Yet, despite the fact that a large portion of the world's population goes to bed hungry at night, and the old ideas prevail that work can be equated with Godliness, we are, in this country, deeply committed through technological and economic advances to a trend that is moving leisure toward the core of life. There is much evidence that we are becoming a leisure oriented society. One indicator of that can be taken from the recent report of a major stockbroker, that the market for leisure goods and services now constitutes about one-sixth of the gross national product, and is annually increasing its share of the G.N.P.

The facts available to us indicate that we are going to have more leisure in the future whether we want it or not. It is not a question of leisure being bad, and therefore we should have less of it; or leisure being good, and therefore we should have more of it. The concern is that leisure may well become the greatest social problem our society has ever faced. When leisure is at the core of life, it will have to be used to give meaning and purpose to our lives, not just pleasurable respite from work as it is viewed by so many of our people today.

Perhaps Russell Lynes, managing editor of _Harpers Magazine_, put the problem in proper perspective when he wrote:

> Since the days of Jamestown and Plymouth, America has had a reverence for work which has been at the root of its entire moral structure. We have honored the toiler in the field and the burner of midnight oil. We have respected the woman whose work is never done and the man who arose early, worked long, dropped into bed exhausted and, we assumed, was satisfied that he had been doing God's work. We opened a continent with work, and we also acquired a kind of moral smugness in the process.
>
> One of the things we were working for was to achieve leisure, and now that we have it, quantities of it, we find ourselves with a curious moral dilemma which it is difficult for us to face. It is a little as though we were a primitive society that had always worked with stone tools and suddenly were presented with mechanized farm implements. Our work is quickly done, our fields are tilled by a few men and a few machines, while others stand around and watch. For a while the millennium seems to have arrived. Then the watchers grow restless, feel useless and distrustful, and they have to change their tribal rites, revamp their moral codes and their social customs and structure, or fly apart as a community.[2]

Is it possible that the current burgeoning attack on our political, economic and social structures, and the moral and ethical values which undergird them, is an outgrowth of freedom from the work ethic? We have, for example, freed our youth, in large measure, from the responsibilities and burdens of work, and in the process have given them time in which to examine and express the values of our society. They have found adult society wanting in its practice of the values they have been taught, and have reacted in various ways--some, in our view, responsibly, and some quite irresponsibly, regardless of their noble motivation. The rule of law is often challenged, and ends now justify means to a large segment of our youthful agents of change.

Fortune magazine some time ago pointed out that the leisure explosion is approximately five times the dimension of the population explosion. For our population is not only increasing--it is securing increased leisure at both ends of the life spectrum, youth and old age, and the shortening work week creates increased leisure in the years between. While it is true that for some segments of our population the work week remains at over 40 hours, for others the work week is decreasing. We are obtaining more and longer vacations, and our holiday weekends are lengthening. The recent Congressional approval of allocating a number of our national holidays to Mondays, following the lead of neighboring Canada, has very interesting social and economic consequences.

Electrical workers in New York recently secured a contract for 26 hours a week, with 6 of those hours being guranteed at overtime pay. Steelworkers and aluminum workers now, upon achieving seniority, receive a bonus of 13 weeks of paid vacation every 5 years. These admittedly, are exceptional examples. But the average American's leisure is also startling. With a 5-day week, two weeks vacation, and 6 national holidays a year, he has 120 days, or about 4 months, of discretionary time! With a 4-day week and 3 weeks vacation, he will have 174 days, or nearly 6 months of discretionary time!

Expressed differently, the average American works 40 hours per week, or nearly 2000 hours per year. Anthony Weiner[3] describes a hypothetical distribution of work and leisure in future years based on 5-day and 4-day work week patterns:

Some Assumed Five-Day Week Working Patterns

Nominal Hours per Week	Legal Holidays	Weeks Off	Total Work Days	Total Days Off	Total Hours
5 x 8 = 40	10	2	240	124	1920
5 x 8 = 40	10	4	230	134	1840
5 x 8 = 40	10	6	220	144	1760
5 x 7.5 = 37.5	10	5	225	139	1687
5 x 7 = 35	10	4	230	134	1610
5 x 7 = 35	10	6	220	144	1540
5 x 7 = 35	10	8	210	154	1470

Some Assumed Four-Day Week Working Patterns

Nominal Hours per Week	Legal Holidays	Weeks Off	Total Work Days	Total Days Off	Total Hours
4 x 7.5 = 30	10	4	184	180	1380
4 x 7.5 = 30	10	6	176	188	1320
4 x 7.5 = 30	10	8	168	196	1260
4 x 7.5 = 30	10	10	160	204	1200
4 x 7.5 = 30	10	12	152	212	1140
4 x 7.5 = 30	10	13	144	220	1080
4 x 7 = 28	10	4	184	180	1208
4 x 7 = 28	10	8	168	196	1096
4 x 7 = 28	10	18	144	220	984

In a leisure-oriented society of the future, then, one could spend 40 percent of his days working, 40 percent of his days on vacation, and 20 percent of his time (or more than one day a week) just relaxing.

Leisure will not be distributed evenly, however. Michaels predicts four leisure classes, and the effects of leisure upon each of them:

Class I

The Unemployed - This class will include people of low educational background, displaced service workers (by cybernation), and well-trained but displaced white collar workers. Feelings of insecurity and uselessness, a low degree of recreational literacy and little desire to do anything about using their leisure will characterize this group.

Class II

Low Salaried Employees Working Part Time - This will include many persons displaced from better paying jobs, a large percentage of whom will be "moonlighters". If these people cannot find second jobs, their problem will be more acute for they will not have the money, the motives or the knowledge to find satisfaction in their leisure. Serious social problems, including frustrating personal relationships, even within families, may result.

Class III

Workers With Good Income, Employed for Shorter Hours - This appears to be the class for whom leisure represents the greatest opportunity. It includes professional, semi-professional, and highly skilled workers. There is expected a fairly high degree of recreational literacy among these people.

Class IV

People With High Income, But Long Work Hours

These will be the top executives and professional personnel, who may well have a high degree of recreational literacy, but comparatively fewer hours of leisure opportunity.[4]

If leisure is a problem for society, however, it is, even more, an opportunity. This statement developed to focus on the educational mission for leisure describes both the problem and the opportunity:

The challenge of leisure, then is that if men and nations learn to live in peace, leisure will be at the core rather than the fringe of life. There will be more people and for many of them earning a living will be only a part-time job. For countless numbers of people incentives heretofore found in work, will have to be found in leisure. Individuals will have more leisure whether they want it or not, and many will be ill prepared to use it. People will be healthier, live longer, and many will have more money to spend. They will be better informed, more sophisticated and more highly educated. Their personal values will be put to the extreme test.

34

They will have to decide not only what they want, but also what they do not want. This may mean much change in heart. Leisure will have to be used for self-fulfillment, for physical and intellectual involvement and cultural development. If it were only a matter of teaching people hobbies, the task would be easy. But changes in values and attitudes, the development of new interests and skills, and a better knowledge and understanding of people in relation to the changing culture are all implied.[5]

The recreative use of leisure, as a way of living, is unescapably related to education at all levels. Therefore much of the responsibility for developing positive approaches to leisure rests with our educational institutions. The university has a 5-dimensional responsibility in relation to leisure:

First, it must create an awareness in all of its students of the challenges, opportunities and problems of leisure as it will affect their lives individually, the social fabric of their communities, the nation and the world community.

Second, it must help prepare people to live, not in a work-centered world, but a leisure-oriented society. This means of course that we must, in our universities, place an increasingly greater emphasis on the transmission of our cultural heritage of art, music, theatre, literature, sports, science, and philosophy, in a manner that helps all people use this heritage in their search for a full life.

Third, it must provide adequate recreation opportunities for students during their years of student residence.

Fourth, it must focus the attention of all disciplines represented in the university upon the problems and opportunities of leisure, and bring to bear their contributions to the solution of the problems of leisure, through interdisciplinary and pan-disciplinary effort, including rigorous scientific investigation. It is this fourth responsibility that has resulted in the proposal to develop a program in leisure sciences at the University of Wisconsin-Green Bay.

Fifth, the university has a clear responsibility to prepare people for professional leisure service occupations, through professional orientation in the undergraduate years and professional specialization in graduate programs.

The responsibility of all educational institutions, but especially higher education, is given special meaning in light of projections for increasing leisure by the prediction (stated some 40 years ago) by a noted economist:

The economic problem, the struggle for subsistence, always has been hitherto the primary, most pressing problem of the human race. If the economic problem is solved, mankind will be deprived of its original purpose.

35

Will this be of benefit? If one believes at all in the real values of life, the prospect at least opens up the possibility of benefit. Yet I think with dread of the readjustment of the habits and instincts of the ordinary man, bred into him for countless generations, which he may be asked to discard within a few decades...thus for the first time since his creation man will be faced with his real, his permanent problem--how to use his freedom from pressing economic cares, how to occupy his leisure which science and compound interest will have won for him to live wisely, agreeably, and well. [6]

The constraints imposed on our satisfying, fulfilling use of leisure are, unfortunately, increasing in proportions similar to the increases in leisure. Our outdoor opportunities, for example, are deteriorating as our needs are expanding. We are polluting our waters, making them unfit for recreational use at a time when the majority of the outdoor recreation seeking population is seeking recreational satisfaction on or near these waters. We are overcrowding our parks, forests, and recreation spaces to such an extent that we are destroying the landscape, and in the process, we are destroying the recreational potential they represent. These constraints, if not corrected, can result, when the leisure opportunity arrives, in making it empty and meaningless.

With the heavy impact of recreation on natural resources already so well established, and with so many indicators that this impact will increase very substantially--it behooves us to examine our current natural resource base for recreation, in terms of quantity, quality, functional usefulness, and our problems in conserving natural resources to provide not only for current use, but for a sustained yield of quality recreation experience.

Some indication of the problem's dimension can be found in our current distribution of recreation lands.

The problem of supply and demand is compounded by the relationship of population distribution to outdoor recreation-use resource distribution. The region of least population has the highest proportion of recreation land.

REGIONAL DISTRIBUTION OF POPULATION, LAND AREA
AND RECREATION ACREAGE

Region	Percentage of Population	Percentage of Land and Water Area	Percentage of Recreation Acreage
West	15	39	72
North Central	29	25	12
South	31	30	11
North East	25	6	4

This comparative lack of outdoor recreation resources close to the populated centers throughout the nation is a major hindrance to satisfying the demand for recreation. The findings of the Outdoor Recreation Resources Review Commission's studies show that the greatest need in recreation resource development is for outdoor recreation opportunities close to home, within travelling distance that permits a day's or less than a day's outing. A massive outlay for the purchase of recreational lands is needed now, for tomorrow will be too late.

The ultimate question is whether leisure will enrich our lives or contribute to the disintegration of our society. The recurring cycle of past civilizations has been well expressed in the Seven Stages of Man.

> Man moves from bondage to faith,
> From faith to courage,
> From courage to freedom,
> From freedom to abundance,
> From abundance to selfishness,
> From selfishness to apathy,
> And down again from apathy to bondage.[8]

No earlier society of man has been able to reverse this trend. If we are to do so, we must recognize the wisdom of Joseph Pieper's statement[9] that leisure is the basis of culture. This calls for a radical change in the values that we have heretofore held sacred.

Addressing myself to the younger people, the students, in this symposium, I would like to pass along one man's[10] suggestion for the kinds of interests, skills, and appreciations that should be developed for the enrichment of man during leisure. He suggested including those activities:

--that help give us a strong spiritual base
--that sharpen our abilities to communicate
   effectively and reflect the social graces
--that aid body development, movement and motor
   coordination
--that contribute to safety and survival (e.g.
   swimming and driving)
--that make use of the creative hands as in the
   graphic and plastic arts
--that take us deep into literature
--that bring us close to nature, and especially
   outdoor living
--that create music, or at least make it possible
   for us to enjoy it
--that provide the opportunity to express ourselves
   through drama in a variety of forms
--that open the doors of the scientific world
   and
--those that encourage us to be of service to others.

There may well be, in the present as well as the future, no commodity more important to us than leisure. Because leisure is time to be used to enrich our lives, each unit of leisure, improperly used, is a lost opportunity--it can never be regained. The recreative use of leisure, then ought to be given special attention. It is our opportunity to live creatively over and over again. It cannot achieve meaning in our lives if we interpret recreation shallowly as amusement, frivolity and aimlessness. It can bring meaning and enrichment to our lives if we recognize that it is inescapably a major factor in the quality of living. To realize leisure's potentials, we must learn how to pursue self-expression, through intellectual, physical and spiritual involvement. Only in this way can the recreative use of leisure become a positive force in our lives--one that is regarded as being at least as honorable as work.

References

*1. Merrill Lynch Pierce Fenner and Smith, The Leisure Market, New York, 1969.

2. Russell Lynes, The Pressures of Leisure, What's New Number 208, The Abbott Laboratories, North Chicago, 1968.

*3. Anthony J. Wiener and Herman Kahn, The Year 2000, The Mac Millan Company, New York, 19

4. Donald Michaels, Cybernation: The Silent Conquest, Center For the Study of Democratic Institutions, Santa Barbara, California, 1962.

5. Edward H. Storey and Charles K. Brightbill, "A Means To Professional Development", Parks and Recreation, Vol. 47, No.5, May, 1954.

*6. John M. Keynes, Essays in Persuasion, W. W. Norton, New York, 1963.

7. Outdoor Recreation Resources Review Commission, Outdoor Recreation for America, Supt. of Documents, Washington, D. C., 1962.

8, 10, Charles K. Brightbill, Self-Fulfillment in a Leisure Oriented Society, unpublished paper, Urbana, Illinois, 1963.

9. Joseph Pieper, Leisure, The Basis of Culture, Pantheon Books, Inc. New York, 1952.

AFTERNOON SESSION

9 January

Chairman - Dr. Alexander R. Doberenz
Assistant Dean, College of Human Biology
University of Wisconsin - Green Bay

Introduction of Dr. Dean E. Abrahamson
Alexander R. Doberenz

Welcome to the second session of this Symposium. The first part of the afternoon's program will be a talk on pollution and population growth. Then , following a brief coffee break, we will have a panel discussion by today's speakers in which the audience is invited to participate. What we want to develop is a dialog between the speakers and the audience, not just among the speakers on the panel.

In the same theme as this morning's talks, which related to the population problems and overview, we have a speaker this afternoon who will talk about pollution and population growth. I am sure you have all heard about how the increasing growth rate is affecting pollution. Our speaker will point out some of the factors which would result from the reverse situation. What effect is pollution having, or what will it have, on population growth?

We are very fortunate to have Dr. Dean Abrahamson to speak on this subject for us. He brings with him a very unique academic background. He has advanced formal training in the physical (physics and mathematics), biological (anatomy) and medical sciences. Because of this multi-disciplinary training, Dr. Abrahamson is extremely well qualified to discuss the relationship between pollution and population growth. Also, he is President of the Board of Directors for the Minnesota Committe for Environmental Information.

So, without any further delay, I will now introduce Dr. Dean E. Abrahamson, who will speak on the "Effects of Pollution on Population Growth".

Effects of Pollution on Population Growth

DEAN E. ABRAHAMSON, M.D., Ph.D.

Department of Anatomy
University of Minnesota Medical School

When Dr. Doberenz graciously asked me to participate in these meetings, he did not specify that the discussions were to center on human populations. If we were to talk of populations of other organisms it would be easy to cite case after case where pollution caused extensive population changes. You need not be reminded of these changes. Wisconsin has been a leader in the evaluations of the use of DDT and related compounds and we all have heard of the effects of these substances on entire species of animals.

There is no question but what pollution and population are very closely related - a relationship which is now being generally recognized. It was only a few years ago that pollution became an acceptable topic for discussion. The extent to which it has entered every-day life is apparent to all and one need only read the advertisements in any periodical to realize that industry is aware of the public's concern. A few years ago the steel companies advertised that they had superior steel; today they are advertising that they have clean effluent streams. In like manner, discussions of population have only recently become acceptable and I think that the realization in the public mind that there is a population problem in the United States has come about largely because of the awareness and concern about pollution and general environmental degredation. This then is the first effect of pollution on population - it has made many Americans, including me, aware that there is a serious problem of overpopulation.

In relating pollution to population, it is misleading to speak of only the number of people as tabulated by the census taker. It is much more meaningful to think in terms of an "effective population". I'll define the effective-population as the actual number of people multiplied by a factor which reflects the impact which they have on their physical environment.

Let us further standardize our effective-population to some standard man, standardized in terms of waste produced. As we look about, it is not unreasonable to select our standard polluter as an individual in Central America, India, Asia or a similar place having a marginal over-all economy and, therefore, relatively little waste per man. Under this definition the "average" American would consume between ten and forty times that of our standard man, and would also, of course, produce ten to forty times the waste.

For purposes of discussion, let us choose a "pollution factor" of twenty-five for Americans. Then instead of considering the population of the United States as something over 200 million, we should consider the "effective population" of the United States as over 5 billion "standard polluters". By this measure, and I think it is valid when considering the effect of man on his physical environment, the United States is grossly overpopulated. We are able to survive in our present condition only by economic colonialism and really are exploiting the natural resources of the world to provide our disposable aluminum beer cans.

We are not alone, certainly other countries are behaving as are we. As will be discussed later, I do not believe that we will be allowed to continue our present course. For the remainder of this talk, please think in terms of "effective population". Also, consider pollution to mean wastes. Pollution has been used to describe many other things since it has become a popular word.

The effects of pollution on population could be described in many ways. It could have an effect on the number of people; it could have an effect on the way the people spend their time; there could be an effect on the distribution of population - that is how they distribute themselves. Pollution can have effects on the jobs available - some industries have gone under because they could not contain their wastes and still make a profit - other industries have arisen because of the need for pollution control equipment. Finally, we could discuss the effects of pollution in terms of some measure of the quality of life.

For the present, I'd like to consider only the effects of pollution on the number of people. There are only two ways which come to mind by which population levels can be changed, by pollution or by anything else. There can be an effect on the number of people born or on the number of people that die.

Considering the number of people born, at least in the United States and other countries which behave as do we, I do not think that there has been any effect because of pollution.

There has, however, been an effect on the number of people who have died, and the effect will become larger. In discussing this it is necessary to consider several age groups - infants, young people, and old people. Let's start with the old people. I personally am not much impressed by statistics of cause of death of, for example, 80 or 90 year-olds. We have largely conquered infectious diseases and a number of other conditions which formerly were major causes of death. We cannot conquer everything; people must die of something and when one is old - suitable old (and I certainly don't know what suitably old is for everyone), then it really does not matter much whether the terminal event is from a condition which can be related to pollution.

I am much more concerned with the number of young people who die and the number of infants who die. There is no question but what respiratory disease is related to air quality and that emphysema and other respiratory diseases are claiming more lives. Respiratory diseases as a whole are increasing rather markedly. Part of it is probably due to smoking, part of it to increasing air pollution.

There is evidence that other conditions, including malignancies, are caused by pollution. Malignancies can be induced by exposure to radioactive wastes, a number of hydrocarbons, and many other substances which are becoming common environmental pollutants. It is very difficult to estimate the numbers of these malignancies. Not only are the risk numbers not well known in many cases, but also the cancer caused by environmental pollutants cannot - except in a few special cases - be distinguished from the cancer which has been induced by other means.

There have been a number of air pollution catastrophies. A prolonged smog in London some years ago lead to a substantial number of deaths; there was an episode in Pennsylvania, and a number of other specific incidents when the number of people who died showed a marked and statistically significant increase. These people died because of pollution. However, the total number is not large when compared to world population and the incidents, until now, have occurred only locally and over fairly restricted time spans.

What I am saying, is that while I am convinced that people are dying from pollution, dying during their youth, I don't think that it is having a significant effect on total population. There is a great deal of speculation about the risks from rising levels of pollutants, but not much documentation - yet.

The situation is similar for infant mortality. The number of infants dying because of exposure to accumulations of wastes, of pollution related diseases, is probably small at least in the United States and Western Europe. It is conceivable, however, that in other parts of the world the sanitary conditions and life which results from accumulation of wastes are significant causes of infant mortality. It has been amply documented that these conditions exist in the United States as well, but to a lesser degree, and I don't think that the statistics are well known.

Again, in my opinion there has not been much effect of pollution on population, at least in the developed countries. We have, however, a very dangerous situation. In many places the water (and air) is fine - there are barely tolerable levels of this - almost insignificant levels of that - industrial wastes at the limit of human tolerance. In many places and under increasingly common circumstances, our environmental situation is such that only a bit more pollution can cause major health problems. I would not at all be surprised were pollution to cause a major public health problem, in the United States, and in the near future.

The question is how much can we tolerate from a purely health standpoint? Pollution control regulations were, to begin with, determined on the basis of navigation. Thou shalt not put so much waste into the river that it would impede navigation. The next step was that Thou shalt not put things in which will cause obvious public health problems. In many instances, the existing regulations have been set somewhat lower than those levels for which we can show an acute effect on man. We have now gone past that step and are beginning to look at it much more rationally. We are beginning to consider - and regulations are being written - standards and regulations not based on acute human exposure, but rather based on chronic exposures, or based on levels that will disrupt the eco-system as a whole.

This brings up another question, and it's something that I wonder about. If, for example, you were going to control the number of people that you had in Wisconsin, how would you do so? It might be done in a number of ways, but is there a critical industry or a critical segment of the population that could be regulated through existing mechanisms? I am thinking about things that would effectively regulate the number of people that you have, or the distribution of those people. Does such an industry exist - for example, the power industry - recognizing, of course, that such a step would have no effect on the world population, and probably only an indirect effect on the population of the United States. I am from Minnesota, and I think Minnesota is one of the best places in the world to live. If you get any farther south, you have to start worrying about molds growing on you; if you get any farther north there are other problems, but I am amazed how few people want to live in Minnesota. Many people who weren't raised here, don't want to come here. I don't think you have to be too discouraged about people not wanting to come to Wisconsin because it's hard to get here anyway and if you take care of the ones that are already here, I really think your problem is much solved. A similar situation doesn't apply to Southern California, or Florida - people somehow manage to convince themselves that those are nice places to live.

What's the evidence of the effect of pollution on other things of interest in this part of the country? Has pollution, for example, had any effect on agricultural practice, or on food production.

Looking at agricultural practice, I contend that it has no effect whatsoever. That the fact that a given agricultural activity pollutes has not to this time had any effect on agricultural practice. The contrary is certainly true, however, agricultural practice has had a profound effect on pollution and on health. In Africa, for example, expanding population and the resultant demands for increased food and power production has lead to the construction of great dams and irrigation works. The impounded water provided many places for snails and has lead to a marked increase in the incidence of schistosomiasis. In this way need for increased food production contributed directly to a major medical problem.

Many regions of the United States are plagued with rapid increases in nitrogen compounds in both surface and ground water. A major, probably the major, source of this nitrogen is agricultural activities. There have been well documented instances of infant deaths due to drinking water with these high nitrogen levels. Once again, the number of deaths has been small, but nitrogen levels continue to increase. There are regions in California where it has been reported that it has been recommended that infants not be given water from local supplies. How long will it be before all of the ground water in agricultural regions has toxic nitrogen levels? Food is not the only output from agriculture!

Population pressure has lead to the development of new strains of various foodstuffs. There is some indication that these new strains require more fertilizer and more DDT, or its counterpart, which, in turn, leads to trouble. The agriculturists who are pushing their increased food production are telling us of only one output; that is, the tons of rice or whatever it is. They are not taking into account the environmental effects because of the need of increased fertilizer, the increased pesticide use, etc. They are telling us only a part of the cost of producing food. Those who might like to read a more detailed speculation along these lines should read the article "Eco-Catastrophe!" by Paul Ehrlich in the September 1969 issue of Ramparts.

Another point is the effect of pollution on medicine, medical education, and the attitude of physicians. Again, I think that except for a very few individuals, there has been no effect. It is my impression that there is probably more time spent on the treatment of hangnails than there is on environmental disease - environmental medicine. That may be a little strong, but I think that it is probably close to the true case. This is occurring at the same time that environmental levels of wastes that have a proven medical human effect are increasing markedly, and I cite pollutants such as DDT, lead, mercury; the list could be made fairly long. The number of toxins known to have an effect on man if the level is high enough, or the exposure is long enough, is increasing rapidly, but the training of physicians does not incorporate this at all. The training of physicians has not, in most instances, recognized the population problem either. For the most part, in medical schools, babies are still great. There is nothing so good as motherhood.

I think that effects of pollution on population, on numbers of people, may be shown in the near future. The level of some environmental wastes, which were thought inocuous, may soon reach levels that are not inocuous. The level of some waste will get so high all over the world that medical effects will begin to show up and everybody will have been exposed. Radiation is one example and DDT another of wastes that do not stay put. These are the things that you have to worry about. A beer can at least stays where you put it. You can throw it along the road and unless somebody picks it up it will stay along the road; you won't find it the next year in Iceland. But there are many wastes which don't behave in that manner and the levels of which are increasing essentially all over the world. Were one of these wastes to reach toxic levels and not be recognized well in advance, we could be in serious trouble.

If we restrict our discussions to waste, pollution meaning waste, I think there has been only a relatively minor effect on population. There is some effect, but it's small, so far; and it may increase markedly. There is also little effect on population distribution so far, but there has been some. What effect there is we see only in highly industrialized societies. If you broaden the definition of pollution as have some, and consider people as a pollutant, then you open up some interesting possibilities. If you would do this, then the effect of having too many people in one place will have profound effect on population through a number of behavioral changes.

We left out one example and that is an effect that I don't think people are aware of, but could lead to a voluntary limiting of family size. Pollution has gotten so bad that everybody knows about it. They begin to talk about it, and somebody mentions that the reason there is all this crap around is because there are too many people. And through pollution awareness, people become aware that there are too many people and will, in fact, do something to limit the future number of people. I don't think that this effect has been noticed yet, but I think that it will - at least I hope so. The reason that I don't think that it's had any effect so far is that pollution itself is still socially acceptable as long as an individual pollutes! It's perfectly alright for an individual to burn trash in his back yard. It's perfectly acceptable for an individual to empty his car ashtray out on the street. The same man who burns trash in his back yard will castigate the local power company because they are polluting. A company can't pollute - that's no longer socially acceptable - an individual still can. Until people begin to carry out their own lives, on an individual basis, to minimize wastes, to minimize the effects of pollution, or to minimize the amount of pollution in their everyday activities - until that happens, I don't think that the number of children which they produce will also be influenced by pollution. And so far there aren't many people who carry out their personal day to day activities such as to minimize their effect on the environment.

People don't buy cars on the basis of how much crap goes out the exhaust pipe. They aren't yet willing to pay the 50¢ a month that it costs to haul away their trash; they prefer to burn it. Until change occurs in pollution practices at an individual level we are not going to see the people limiting family size because of pollution.

Now, what can we do about it? And it's quite simple what you can do about it. First, you have to become informed. This is work. A lot of people come to lectures, hear pollution talks, then go home, go about their business as usual. That's not enough. It's nice - kind of like going to church - to go to hear a pollution man talk from time to time. We then go back home and sin as usual, and go home and burn your trash just like we always did. It's nice and socially acceptable to come in the morning and say "you know, I was at a pollution talk last night". But that's not enough. We must, as I suggested before, change our own style of life. Each of us must do things which we can do. Some of us can do more than others - some are in a position to do a great deal. Educators, chairmen of boards, owners of industrial establishments, physicians - can influence others while most of us can only influence ourselves and our immediate families. We can all, however, make our wishes known to our elected officials and to the local polluters. We can all become reasonably informed about pollution and population problems and discuss them with our friends. To do less is to totally ignore our responsibilities.

Scientists and other professionals have been for the most part singularly remiss in their treatment of environmental and population problems. They have been all too willing to talk about the pollution and population problems over the coffee table, or to their peers. They write learned articles for journals. In order to get an article published in a journal it cannot be in English, it has to be in some lingo, which is characteristic of the particular discipline. When someone does write something in English and publishes it in the daily newspaper, he is criticized as exhibiting not very academic behavior. We have been singularly remiss in not talking with the public, in English, about the problem. This situation is changing, however, and I think you should do what you can to encourage it. Ask your scientists and engineers to learn Anglo-Saxon English and to speak with people who are not scientists or engineers. People have to be aware of what's going on; why, and what they can do about it. It's not enough that I'm aware of it and that my colleagues at the University are aware of it; you have to be aware, your elected officials have to be aware.

Most of the problems are not scientific problems. This is not to say that none of them are, but most of them aren't. The control of environmental pollutants is not a technical problem in most cases. It's a social, economical and political problem. The technology exists. What doesn't exist is the willingness to spend another dime. Sewers have never been a popular campaign issue. Stockholders like to hear about profit and growth rather than they like to hear about the effectiveness of cleaning up waste. I think the same thing applies to population. Thank you.

GENERAL READING SOURCES:

The Population Bomb, by Paul Ehrlich. Ballantine 1968 (paperback)

The Web of Life, by J. Storer, Signet, (paperback)

Science and Survival, by Barry Commoner, Viking (paperback)

"Address to the University of Notre Dame", by Robert S. McNamara,
May 1, 1969. Up to 25 copies available without cost from the World
Bank, 1818 H Street, Washington, D.C. 20433

"People Pollution" in Medical World News, December 19, 1969.

"Overpopulated America", by W. H. Davis, in The New Republic,
January 1970

Panel Discussion

Dr. Alexander R. Doberenz - Chairman

Dr. Irene B. Taeuber

Dr. Paul Gyorgy

Dr. E. H. Storey

Dr. Dean E. Abrahamson

Mr. David Greenwood,
Sophomore Student, UWGB

DR. DOBERENZ:

Before we conduct our panel discussion, I would like first to take just a minute to remind you of the purpose of this. It is to build a dialog between you, the audience, and the speakers. So we anticipate a lot of questions and the panel members are very willing to answer them. I would like to say, based on what happened earlier this morning, that it is very difficult to pick up some of the questions in the back. We have a man back there with a microphone, so when you have a question, please raise your hand, and before stating it, please wait until he gets there with the microphone. We would appreciate it also if you would give your name and affiliation if you feel that it's relevant to the panel. You have the advantage - you know exactly who the panel members are and what their background is and they know very little about you. Also, this panel discussion will be included in the proceedings. Therefore, we want to make sure that we pick up the question. It is very difficult later on to go back and make up a question to fit the answer that has been given. If for any reason you do not wish to give your name, then just state anonymous. This way I will not keep asking you if you will please give your name.

To introduce the members of the panel who I am sure you are all familiar with now - Dr. Taeuber, Dean Storey, Dr. Gyorgy, Dr. Abrahamson and Mr. David Greenwood. Dave is a student at UWGB, a sophomore, who is very interested in this problem, and who has just recently completed one of our courses which covers essentially this area of population growth. He is here to give, in essence if you request, the student view or opinions. They may not necessarily be his own, but he will give you what his generation feels about the question.

I was going to have each of the members give a position statement but I don't think that will be necessary. I notice that the attendance has not fluctuated or changed so I assume that almost everyone here has heard all of the talks this morning. Thus, I think that it would be unnecessary to ask them to give a position statement. I will immediately throw this discussion open to the floor now, starting in the back of the room because I think the microphone is there.

PAUL HAYES (Milwaukee Journal):

I have a question for Dr. Abrahamson. You mentioned in your talk that medical training shows serious deficiencies in regard to the possible medical effect of environmental pollution. Why is that and what can be done about it?

DR. ABRAHAMSON:

I prefaced the remark with "the schools with which I am familiar". There may very well be many schools in which environmental problems are adequately treated. Physicians who are now running the medical schools grew up in an age when this wasn't really an important problem; at least it wasn't recognized as such. Much of what they were told, what they think, etc. was engraved in stone in their minds long ago. They, like the rest of us, change slowly. I think this is a major reason. Another reason is that it hasn't been a really popular subject until recently. It's only recently that it has been socially acceptable to talk about wastes - that applies equally well to medical schools as it does to newspapers. Perhaps, the time constant for change in a medical school is longer than it is in some other places.

DR. DOBERENZ:

You said you had another question.

PAUL HAYES:

Yes, if you want to get to it now. You also posed the hypothesis that maybe an area or a state could have a single industry, the manipulation of which could control population growth or population decline, and as I recall it, you mentioned the electric utility. Why did you single out the electric utility?

DR. ABRAHAMSON:

Because I think that it might be the one industry that can be handled in this way - at least in this area. Another reason is that the quality of waste correlates much more with the rate of growth of power use than it does with just the number of people. I think if you could choose one in-dustry - and this may be complete nonsense for all I know, it may be that this won't work and that it doesn't amount to anything - but it seems that if you were going to make a list the power industry would be quite high on the list.

DR. LEONARD WEIS (UWGB):

This is a general question. Dr. Abrahamson gave us some references for guidance. I wonder if all of the panel could provide for the proceedings a short list of annotated references. For example, I am completely ignorant on the social history of the Far East; the history books I read did not give the kind of information we learned this morning.

GEORGE HOWLETT (Door-Kewaunee County Teachers College, Algoma):

Dr. Abrahamson, you said that you didn't think there was any effect of air pollution on agriculture, or I think you made a comment to that effect. And, I am wondering if you have come across any references to the fact that smog and other air pollutants may be affecting the rate of photosynthesis which would have a serious effect on the rate of oxygen production?

DR. ABRAHAMSON:

I don't think I said that. At least I didn't mean to. What I thought I said was that I don't think that pollution resulting from agricultural practices has had much effect on agricultural practice. Air pollution has a major effect on many crops. This is well documented, but is another story. I didn't mean to give the impression that there was no effect of pollution on agriculture.

DR. JERRY COMBS (Center for Population Research, N.I.H.):

We seem to be picking on Dr. Abrahamson, but his talk is fresh in our minds and my question has to do with the fact that he is concentrating on the measurable effect on mortality, etc. He did not mention the effects of pollutants of various kinds on the quality of life and I think maybe he would like to expand on that. I wish he would.

DR. ABRAHAMSON:

I will answer that in two ways. Pollution results in increase in the amount of irritation. People get irritated by other people, by many other things, by crowding, and such things, but also irritability is increased by, for example, lead levels. You pick up a little more lead, you get a little more irritable - at least in a physiological sense. We are seeing a great deal of this now in many ways. Things that irritate us add up until finally socially unacceptable behavior results. There are many examples.

The other thing is the business of "quality of life". I personally think that the standard of living in the United States is dropping - it's going down very rapidly and it has been going down for some time. It probably peaked, at least in the way I think about it, in the early 1900's and since then we have been on the way down. We don't often stop to define what quality of life means. What choices are removed by various actions which go towards making more plastic bottles, or their equivalent? I am convinced that there is a large segment of the population who equate "quality of life" with living in a plastic box with air piped in and wastes piped out, and the natural environment, as we know it, is completely meaningless to them. There are many people who think that the standard of living is measured in terms of the number of cars you have, the amount of waste you produce, etc. I don't share those views.

DR. WILLIAM KAUFMAN (UWGB):

Dr. Taeuber, this morning I believe inferred that you perhaps felt that there was an upper limit to the population - the Oriental populations - and you mentioned that demographers in the United States had forecast that we would reach an upper limit within the United States back in the 1930's which obviously we didn't do. Would you comment on this a bit? Do you feel that there will be an upper limit to the Oriental populations and to that of the United States; and then perhaps we could go on to Dr. Abrahamson who gave me the impression that he felt the other way, that the upper limit would come only with a great tragedy.

DR. TAEUBER:

The figures that I cited this morning were not, in fact, for the world and for the Asian countries. They were not American estimates. They were, in fact, the United Nations' estimates. If you would like me to crawl out on a limb, I am fairly certain there will not be 7-1/2 billion people in the world thirty years from now. Neither I, nor any of the Indians or Pakistani that I know, see how these economies are to develop to support one billion people in India and Pakistan in the year 2000. Now, on the question of upper limits, I am glad you brought this up. The question of how many people there will be in the future depends of course on what happens to birth rates and what happens to death rates. Populations below those projected can come either through declines in the birth rate, or through increases in the death rate. If you move from this and try to assess what is likely to happen as contrasted with some form of a hypothetical upper limit, then you have to bring in all kinds of other variables. Let's take the Hindu - Pakistan sub-continent. If the sciences and technologies that are related to caloric production were all applied, then I think that it would be possible to triple or quadruple food production on this subcontinent. Will those or will not those be applied? If they are applied, then will they be applied under so-cial arrangements so that the increase in production - the increase in income - is shared by the peoples of the countries, or will they result in a further stratification of the social structure and further political instabilities? This is in the area of food production. In the area of the level of the birth rate, the government of India has been committed since 1952, and the government of Pakistan has been committed in the last several years to family planning programs to reduce the birth rate. Now, in theory, the techniques of birth control which are now available should permit the development of programs which would reach the people and result in declines in fertility. If you go into, shall we say, the social area, the sciences and technologies that are now available in means of communications, in means of instruction, should again offer possibilities for the education of all of the people. Now, whether these things do or do not happen are, I suspect, all interre-lated and the question of the upper limit on the numbers of the people de-pends fundamentally on whether there is, or is not, economic and social de-velopment progress in solving family and child-bearing habits. I probably have already answered too long, but let's put it this way. In the early 19th century, the United States of America had a birth rate of 55. We had a death rate of around 25 or 30. We were growing by natural increase alone 3% a year, and in the century from 1790 to 1890, we secured and occupied an entire continent. We also had millions and millions of immigrants pour-ing in from Europe. In other words, the high rate of population growth is not an inherent problem. It is a problem because of the setting in which it is occurring, because of what it means for the quality of the training and the living for these children.

DR. DOBERENZ:

Dr. Abrahamson, do you want to make a comment or rebuttal?

DR. ABRAHAMSON:

I have two comments, one prompted by the remarks which we just heard. If food production is going to increase substantially a chain of events follows. Food production can be increased by a more intensive agriculture or you can suddenly find more land, and the amount of land in the world is fixed. If one opts for more intensive agriculture - that means large areas with intensive cropping of a single crop. Whenever there is a simple arrangement like this with a very small number of species present, one has a very unstable system from an ecological standpoint. Efforts to keep the insects away - in order to keep the crops growing - then lead to increased uses of pesticides, which leads to trouble in many, many ways. There are similar arguments involving fertilizers, land use --- . And so, again, those who are making fantastic claims about the increase in agricultural production, are only totalling up part of the output and are misleading us.

Now, the question about the upper limit of population in the world - obviously there is an upper limit. There is a finite size world. There is a finite number of people. There is going to be a steady state of population, or at least an equilibrium level. I think that the equilibrium level will be substantially lower than the population that now exists. One recent study assumed that everybody in the world had a standard of living equal to the middle class American, defined as between $12,000 to $15,000 per family per year, and looked at the amount of resources it took to sustain it. That is, everybody in the world would be living as a family in the United States having an income of $12,000 to $15,000. With that assumption the analysis indicated the world could support 500 million people in a steady state. That's a lot fewer than we now have.

I think that control of the population by rational methods is quite unlikely and so wouldn't be surprised if it is controlled by other than rational means (unless you consider widespread destruction of people by one means or another rational). Hopes for a rational population policy are slim. Increasing population is leading to instabilities of various kinds. There is going to be a ruckus within our lifetime as a result.

DR. RONALD J. PION:

I raised my hand before Dr. Abrahamson discussed the corrupt of a world with a finite carrying capacity. It is something that all of us must begin to think about. The scientist hasn't yet translated what the phrase means. It is difficult to do this because we have never sat down and asked questions like what is the optimal population size - for Seattle, Washington or for Green Bay, Wisconsin. It's going to be terribly embarrassing in our own communities to suddenly find out that we have surpassed the optimum. People on a space ship, traveling anywhere, have a finite carrying capacity. The people on the planet earth must realize that the planet earth has a finite carrying capacity, and although biblically we were all asked to be fruitful, to multiply, and replenish the earth, we really ought to sit down and ask if we have already done it.

DR. TAEUBER:

I do not have a rebuttal, but I would like to speak here. Let's assume that when we say the word "we" that we are an Indian panel, sitting in the University of Lucknow and are now being questioned by the people of Lucknow. Now, I think this is more relevant to the levels of living that are regarded as feasible - to the questions of the future - than the assumption that the rest of the world either has a chance to, or shall we say should, become middle class Americans. I don't think there is a future, whether a götter-damerung or salvation, which is world wide in the next thirty to forty years. Let us look at the question of India. You people would be willing to say that there are more Indians now in India than would ideally have been located in that country. Can you now say that there is no way out for India other than a vast destruction of people through famine, epidemic, or revolution. It is this kind of question that makes me unwilling to deny the possibility of ways through the difficulties in which countries now are. Perhaps, I'm just cowardly, but I cannot say there is no other way than having half the people die.

DR. ABRAHAMSON:

Just a minor comment. Dr. Taeuber is perfectly right, but if you assume that the world lives at the level we do and you arrive at a small number of people and you have a larger population now, it follows then that the average level of consumption will be lower than we now have. The next thing in the argument, of course, is that our standard of living will decrease from what it is now. I think that we peaked some time ago.

DR. TAEUBER:

The world is not a community. In my hypothetical panel which is meeting in the University of Lucknow, I am certain we would all be willing to settle for a Taiwanese level of living.

DR. ABRAHAMSON:

Fine, but you decide this on a nation by nation basis, or whatever it is.

DR. TAEUBER:

That's what I am trying to get across.

58

DR. ABRAHAMSON:

I don't dispute that at all. The ultimate population for each nation is that population which that nation can feed or support. The idea that a country is going to get 60% of what it eats by importing it - that game isn't going to last much longer.

DR. WEIS:

I would like to ask each of the panelists, starting with Mr. Greenwood, to carry this point a little bit farther. What does each mean by quality of life, both in terms of our own society here, and how we should look at it in terms of other societies - not just a mythical one.

MR. GREENWOOD:

Quality of life to me, I guess, would mean simply the way in which the person you are taking under consideration is living. I mean I am not versed in the technical knowledge, but I would suggest possibly: does he have enough to eat, is he cold, does he have a roof over his head, is he happy - things like this. Superior quality of life would probably then be superior in the needs of the person, and excessive quality would be whether he has 3 cars, or 2 boats, or whatever. From my point of view, this is how I would look at a man's quality of life - it's how he's living. It's how the person goes through life. Is he starving to death? Naturally, he is not then happy - he doesn't have enough to eat, or clothes, etc. There are different qualities throughout the world of course.

DR. ABRAHAMSON:

A nasty question. I will start answering it with a little story. There is a symposium now meeting at the University of Minnesota; it started in September and it is going to run on through this school year. We are supposed to advise the State Planning Agency on how they would advise the rest of the state, the administration, etc., how to preserve the environment of Minnesota. Well, this panel of learned experts absolutely refuses to sit down and discuss this basic question. You can't recommend for the future until you define what you want for the future, and they absolutely refuse to talk about it.

To me "quality of life" means, among other things, that you preserve options available to each man. If a man and his family want to live in the woods, they can still find some woods. If they want to eat fish, they can still find some fish. If they want to eat meat, there is a little meat available. If they want to have a cat, there is going to be food for his cat, and this kind of thing. We are running out of these options. To define "quality of life" as just keeping people clothed and fed and warm is entirely unacceptable. We could do this by making the little plastic box of which I spoke earlier, but I don't think many people would be happy in it.

MR. GREENWOOD:

I think I mentioned when I said that the man should be happy. In my layman terms, I tried to say what Dr. Abrahamson was saying. Happiness to me would mean more than eating, sleeping, being - I would have to have more than that.

DR. ABRAHAMSON:

My remarks were not directed at my colleague.

DR. GYORGY:

It is apparently easier to ask questions than to answer them. I belong apparently to the group of colleagues at the symposium at the University of Minnesota who refuses to answer this question, except for one modification. I think it is obvious that living conditions will change everywhere, and for each country they will find something different. In spite of the improvement in communications, Taiwan will not follow the American System for a long time, and so on. I am a born optimist and I will die an optimist. And I personally think that we will find a solution within the limits which we discussed. It doesn't mean that the population explosion should continue, but I think for instance Dr. Abrahamson dismissed it with a one-half sentence concerning the possibility of food from the ocean. Well, I am not as pessimistic about it. I know many colleagues, experts in marine resources, and in their field they feel that there is much, much more food that agriculture would be able to produce. I am not talking about the algae, but algae is also a food. And I am not talking of chemically produced food, such as amino acids and protein which also are possible. I reserve judgment - I don't know whether I will live as long, but I don't want to leave this symposium as a converted pessimist.

DR. STOREY:

I will agree that this is a pretty sticky question, and I don't believe that any one man can describe for another what the quality of his life ought to be. I suspect that we will have to reach some understanding of the kinds of quality of life that people expect, the aspirations that people have, by studying the collective behavior, the collective interests, the collective attitudes of people in different regions, in different cultures, in different socio-economic classes, even people of different ages. In the field of leisure, for example, a person who will accept swimming in the muddy waters of the Mississippi will not be the same person who has been brought up to the superior quality of water that can be found in Wisconsin's White Potato Lake, 60 miles north of Green Bay. We perceive quality differently, and as such I wouldn't want to attempt to define any one standard of quality of life.

DR. TAEUBER:

I will move far out. I am a realist, and answer in terms of the less developed Asian countries, in terms of Latin America and North Africa. When we - or when I say - quality of living in this context, I refer to minimum requirements. The first is minimum adequate nutrition. Then there is shelter from the elements, some minimum levels of health and vitality, opportunities to work, a social structure that permits dignity, and a political system that permits some justice under law. These are minimum bases for quality in any culture; the pluses beyond these in accord with the values of the cultures.

DR. ABRAHAMSON:

I am not an expert in the food from the oceans. I know only what I read and I don't think I read only the crackpots, but maybe I do. I get the distinct impression that the ultimate amount of food that we will be able to harvest from the ocean is only a few times what is now being harvested - where a few times is probably three or something like that. If we start to eat the shrimp and the algae - then obviously we can extract more protein, but I don't think it's anything like some of our more optimistic colleagues would have us believe.

Now, I want to raise another question. If you accept, as the panel seems to, that the standard of living defined anyway you like, will not be the same in all countries, I am just curious if, for example, Central Americans will permit the present ratio of consumption in the United States to that in their countries to continue to exist. Will they tolerate living next to a country which is singularly more affluent than they are? I am just curious. I personally think they won't.

DR. PION:

Well, they will. Dean, they will if you don't let television get to Central America and you don't let anybody travel to that country so that they don't ever find out what is going on elsewhere. Dr. Gyorgy, I too am an optimist. I am a younger optimist than you are. But I feel that our optimism - our collective optimism - must be tempered for example unless we call a moratorium to birth beginning today and feeding all of the malnourished children of the world that are alive today. Once we have succeeded in feeding all of the malnourished children of the world, optimizing their condition, then let us reinvite other children into the world as we can provide for them. What troubles me, and perhaps what troubles Dean, if I understand his statements correctly - is the continuing optimism which does nothing but dampen, or occlude, in the minds of the great masses of the people what the significance and magnitude of the problem are all about.

The botanists met this summer in my fair city of Seattle and they talked of food chains, and they talked of agriculture and a green revolution, and then a group of students came up from Berkeley and said some pretty strong things - and passed around a petition - and asked the botanists to take a very hard look at the kind of food chains that really could bring about optimal standards of nutrition throughout the world. Those collective, learned people - perhaps under pressure we might say - made their statement "let's go about and begin to solve the population problem - not talk - but

61

try and solve it", and concurrently continue talk about increasing the nutritional demands of people. If I could share a fantasy with all of you for a moment, I would declare Calcutta a model city, that we, as a unity in the world, work on, beginning next month - because we need some planning time. We will take pictures of Calcutta now, and then we will take pictures of Calcutta in ten years after the experts of the world have an opportunity to utilize funds and expertise and knowledge in doing something about the visceral reaction all of us have when we are visiting in Calcutta. Let us activists change the face of Calcutta, but not so every man in Calcutta has $12,000 to $15,000 as his annual income. Let's ask the people of Calcutta what they would like in their model city, and then let's redirect our moon shot money and a lot of other defense money that we are spending - to bring about a change in Calcutta because then we can hold up to the peoples of the world a before and after picture of Calcutta.

DR. GYORGY:

Dr. Pion, I don't think that we have any difference between us. I fully agree with everything that you have said. My whole policy, for instance, is to improve Calcutta and Calcutta-like cities and agricultural communities in the world. I personally believe, however, that with regard to the remark about Central and Latin America, what is needed is proper distribution of the means of living. In Mexico which has made tremendous progress, I think the situation still requires urgent improvement. Whether local land reform alone would do it, I doubt, but certainly it's one of the points one has to consider. The living conditions in Central and Latin America can be vastly improved in a relatively short period of time. We should not be afraid, but we should not offer them the kind of help as we have done in the past by telling them what to do. They should do it through self help.

DR. ABRAHAMSON:

I am glad you brought up that last point. Many have observed that we have been extremely clever in the way we offer aid to other countries. The first thing we do - forget the missionaries for the moment - is send in medical people and eliminate infectious diseases - it's pretty easy to run around and immunize everybody. So the first thing you do is you keep the kids alive, then we help educate them so they find what bad shape they are really in. The result is a lot of people who are not going to die of infectious diseases, or these things that are easily controlled, who realize, with the help of the television and the transistor radio, how bad off they are compared with others. Then we wonder about giving aid to develop industries, to employ themselves, etc., etc., etc. It seems that the developmental aid is just opposite to what it should be.

MR. HOWLETT:

Since the upper limit of population - the theoretical upper limit of population - would be determined by the standard of living, and the higher the standard the lower the theoretical limit, should we not have a stop to new needs being created by our advertising media?

62

DR. DOBERENZ:

Is that directed to anyone in particular?

DR. GYORGY:

To Madison Avenue perhaps.

DR. ABRAHAMSON:

Yes, I think it's stupid. I have been working on the power industry. I don't work on them - I rather snipe at them from time to time - but there is a perfect example. A power company comes and says that power needs are increasing; it's doubling every six years. I think one reason they are doubling every six years is because they are building plants to double it every six years, exactly as your question implies. I think we should stop the Madison Avenue tactics until we have thought about it. Maybe after we have thought about it, we will say it's great - let's go on and do it, but let's do it on at least a semi-rational basis, and not the way it is now.

MR HAYES:

I am a little away from my field and I am not working now as a reporter but doesn't the way to curtail the artificial creation of needs really lie in the attitudes of consumers? Do we really need an electric power lint remover and things like that? Isn't that the attitude? If you curtail the advertising media you could do it from one or two directions. You can do it from above - from a governmentally imposed campaign - or you can do it by simply what you said, Dr. Abrahamson, and that's re-educating the consumer as to what kind of a world he wants to live in. It seems to me that pollution goes back to the individual and the individual is the polluter and when he buys his incredible array of electrically powered apparatus that do everything except raise his head from the pillow in the morning, he's polluting. Maybe that's a speech and not a question.

DR. ABRAHAMSON:

The start is by asking the question, and until recently the question has not been asked - at least not publically. We ought to ask it and talk about it.

DR. BENHAM:

We heard just this afternoon something about pollutors - man as pollutors and all that - but I didn't hear before anything about man as a pollutant himself, and I was thinking about the phrase of the teeming refuse. I don't know if I got it right. But if that were the case, I would hate to be the one to decide who was the refuse - the extra one to dispose of. Taking that apart, I wanted to refer to Dr. Storey's talk this morning - a very inspiring talk about the use of leisure time and how much there is going to be and already is. I couldn't help but think at the time that this represents the possibility of man living in one place and going to a second place for his recreation, and as we saw, frequently by water. I am more concerned, however, with - and my question follows - the person who has only one place to be, and I wonder whether we are going to be ready, say in a sparsely populated state like Wisconsin, for the great out migration of people who have to leave other parts of the country, particularly the Eastern megalopolis, in order to find the one place to live. Are we going to be ready for a redistribution, whether voluntary or not, for people who are actually fleeing to what is still the much purer water and air that you find in the middle and western parts. Are we prepared for this? I wonder if Dean Storey would like to talk about that for a bit?

DR. STOREY:

It's a very sticky question again, Dr. Benham. I will attenpt to deal with it from the standpoint of the way we plan and the way we implement the plans that are made for us - and refer to it in the leisure context. I think that it is apparent at the moment that we will not be ready, if there were to be an out-migration from the major population centers today to Wisconsin. We have not recognized at this point, as I see it in the State of Wisconsin - and I think this is true of most areas of the country - the fact that a burgeoning demand for recreation is upon us, and that we should be preparing for it. Dr. Pion mentioned the need for better understandings of carrying capacities. From the leisure standpoint, I think we need to begin to plan for the State of Wisconsin and for all of our recreation lands on the basis of some understanding of people as pollutants in the leisure environment.

In other words, I think that there are a certain number of people who can be impacted in a certain resource area and when you get beyond that level, the quality of the human experience diminishes because of what might be called "people pollution." We need to plan from the standpoint of understanding the impact of those people who might be able to stand each other in a given amount of space, but there might be too many people in that given amount of space to enable them to use the resource space and have the resource sustain the particular use to which it is being put. This is why we need such people as Dr. Mowbray here, or Dr. White, for example, who help us understand the relationship between the carrying capacity of lands and their recreational uses for people. We need people in social psychology to help us understand the attitudes of people towards their recreational experiences. That is what I meant when I said we must understand the collective behavior of people, their collective attitudes and their collective interests, because only on that basis can we plan intelligently. That's a rather quick answer to a very involved question, but my answer is no - I don't think we are ready; I don't think we know at this point how to plan effectively.

DR. ABRAHAMSON:

You have a laboratory in upper New England and you can watch closely what's happening right now. Vermont, New Hampshire and Maine are now facing this very thing and are talking about it at a state administrative level - and at a legislative level. I think that it is good to watch what happens there - because we in Minnesota and you in Wisconsin are not far behind - we can at least profit by their experience before the crowd comes here.

MR. JOHN MANNING:

I am John Manning, a retired machinist, retired on social security. I have a question for Dr. Paul Gyorgy on nutrition and chemistry. Are synthetic Vitamins A, and synthetic Vitamins B_1, B_2, B_6 and B_{12} as effective and beneficial as the natural vitamins that are derived from natural sources, such as plants, berries, vegetables, etc.?

DR. GYORGY;

It reminds me of a hearing before the Food and Drug Administration on this very problem. The representative of the health food people asked me the same question. I don't know how to answer it differently. These are chemical entities. All chemical and physical qualities have proved their composition and the synthetic products are the mirror image - or the image - indeed absolutely the same as natural vitamins, and they have the same effect. There cannot be any difference between the natural vitamin and a synthetic vitamin.

MR. MANNING:

Synthesizing them would be beneficial to solving the world's nutrition problems wouldn't it?

DR. GYORGY:

I mentioned before that amino acids and vitamins can be synthesized; carbohydrates can be synthesized; fats can be synthesized; and it's one of the reasons that I am an optimist. Maybe we don't have as much fun as eating oranges and good steak, but we could survive.

DR. RONALD STARKEY (UWGB):

I think that the difference between synthesis and creation must be distinguished here. They have to be synthesized from somewthing which requires a natural resource, and you can't just create them. We have to have a source of the chemicals to produce artificial vitamins.

DR. GYORGY:

Most of them can be produced from natural products like coal, charcoal, petroleum and these type of products, and there are sources available, I think without any limit, to produce them. Well, fairly unlimited. The whole situation reminds me - I cannot resist mentioning it - of Malthus, who 100 years ago, stated that we are at the end of the world, and we are not yet at the end of the world. I think that we should never forget the mistake of Malthus.

DR. STARKEY:

He only missed it by 100 years maybe.

DR. GYORGY:

You think that we are at the end of the world now?

DR. STARKEY:

I am not optimistic.

DR. GYORGY:

Well, you are younger and you will probably live longer to prove that we are not at the end of the world.

DR. WENDEL JOHNSON (UWGB):

Dr. Abrahamson talked earlier about the effects of pollution on population growth. We hear a great deal about the air and the water pollution. One of the frightening things that is coming to the front now is noise pollution. I am wondering if anyone on the panel, particularly Dr. Abrahamson, has any information to suggest what this might do to population growth. It certainly has effects on population.

DR. ABRAHAMSON:

Another irritant - noise has an effect in two ways that I know. One is the actual physical damage to the ear. You can be exposed to noise such that it destroys your ability to hear. After that happens the noise doesn't bother you any more. The other thing is that noise just adds to the other irritants that are increasing because of too many people in one place. Noise is particularly easy to handle because it can be easily controlled if you try. One problem has been that few machines seem to have been designed to minimize noise. You must realize that it is cheaper to build an engine that will clank a little than it is to machine it up so that it runs quietly; and if we want to pay enough to redesign the equipment to silence things, if we want to pay more for our homes so that we can have it quiet inside, we can. It is becoming a problem because we haven't been willing to pay to remove it.

DR. GYORGY:

In the State of Wisconsin - I cannot resist making a remark - I remember very well, maybe it was about 20 years ago, that records were being played to "contented" dairy cows and the claim was made that the milk production increased.

DR. STOREY:

I would like to add one to that. In Normal, Illinois, a farmer tried playing different kinds of music to corn and claims to have proven that restful, quiet music will greatly assist in the more rapid growth of corn crops.

66

DR. KAUFMAN:

There has been a Birtish study published recently. It was done over many, many years and by a great number of British groups, who showed that noise has no measurable effect whatsoever in any way on their populations. They didn't quite know how to do this but when they added noise to workers' rooms the workers worked better. Production went up. This, of course, simply may be that they paid attention to the people. But they did find that around airports and around London there were no more sleeping pills sold than there were in areas where there was not extensive noise. Of the thousands of people questioned only about 14% listed noise as one of the things they would change if they could; and the highest percentage, if I remember, that wanted to change something, if they could, 17% would change the noise of adult human voices.

MISS RUTH JOST:

Dr. Taeuber, do you think that there is a causal relationship between the political upheavals in Southeast Asia and the decline of population?

DR. TAEUBER:

One of my great desires is to get some number one caliber political science students who will pursue their way through graduate school into research in the area of demographic political relations. There is practically no research. If one takes the relation between increasing numbers per se and specific political events, then there are major questions. I will limit myself now to the Asian setting, though there are comparable arguments for the United States. The precipitant declines in death rates began about twenty years ago; the lives that were saved were mainly those of infants and young children. What are the associations between the almost tidal wave of youth maturing in Asian countries and the difficulties in their universities and among their students? The effects of increasing attendance and increasing numbers are compounded. I am not saying there are relationships; I am saying this is an area for research. Similarly, as I mentioned this morning, the Red Guards who are aroused and then sent to the countryside in the People's Republic of China represented the increased numbers of middle school students for whom there were no positions in the communes, or in agriculture, or in the cities. In this complex, there may have been a push toward political instability.

There is another relationship which political scientists might explore. In Indonesia and Malaya, the problem of not only political stability but the maintenance of the political system itself is related directly to the problems of cultural divisiveness. The divisions within India and the rates of growth are interrelated factors of instability. On whether there are relations between growth itself and political instability or revolution, I will make one comment. In world history, it has generally been the more advanced and the somewhat less deprived people who have engaged in revolution. The classic example is the American colonies. Ours were the most prosperous and best treated colonial colonies in the world at the time, but we were the

67

first to rise in true rebellion for an abstract principle of taxation without representation.

There are truly serious aspects to this if we are talking about what governments should do. There are real questions as to how much a government can move ahead of its population and force birth control on a people who may not be ready for it.

DR. GYORGY:

In order to avoid any misunderstanding with Dr. Taeuber, in the research for which you would like to have a political scientist, I assume and I hope, that you mean a national political scientist and not an American.

DR. TAEUBER:

I will have to answer that by saying that I am certain that even Lloyd's of London would not issue insurance on an American political scientist who went into Kuala Lumpur to study the relations between the Chinese population, civil tensions, and violence in depth. This is an area of research which has to be done within the country.

DR. GYORGY:

I am afraid your statement that it has to be done within the country is ambiguous. If I would go to these countries, I am within the country.

DR. TAEUBER:

By Nationals within the country. It has to be done by Nationals within the country whose base is an institution within the country and who do not have grants with any of the circulating funds of the U. S. Government, and, preferably, who have no funds to trace directly or indirectly to any American sources.

DR. ABRAHAMSON:

We must not confuse study with doing something about the problem. It reminds me of the comment by a graduate student in cultural anthropology who was studying groups that were doing things. He said that "it has occurred to us lately that we are studying the groups who are doing what we should be doing". I wonder if that's not relevant to some of the social science research programs.

DR. PION:

Here again, one of the nicest things about Dr. Gyorgy and Dr. Taeuber is, as the Vista slogan goes, "if you're not working on the solution, you're part of the problem". Fortunately, and happily, you people are working on the solution. All of us working on the solution hopefully are not part of the problem. I think what Dr. Abrahamson again said during his talk is important to consider - how do we get everybody working on the solution so that we all are not part of the problem? I will happily take part of the responsibility for helping to put "people pollution" on the cover of Medical World News for having suggested that the excellent environmental series end with "people pollution" amd "people as pollutants". These are terribly emotive phrases - the refuse heap, and which part of it shall we do away with. The suggestion that I would have, and I hope to be able to elaborate on it more tomorrow, is let's solve the problems of all of the peoples of the world, as I say in a fantasy, now. Let's stop the accidental conception of children. One of our problems - and for my special colleagues and I say "special" using the concept of the word species, my special colleagues in the clergy, whom I would like to hear from today or tomorrow, is that we have not separated sex from procreation as a human function. Religion has a great obligation to help the human species understand the differences between sex and procreation. Sex is sinful only in the dirty minds of adults. It's not sinful in the minds of children. As an obstetrician, I have never delivered a child who is a bigot. Adult behavior serves as a model for the behavioral development of children. What we do as adults in our own community has great telling effect on how kids grow up. We have no validity and credibility in the developing rationale around the world in the area of birth control, or in the euphemism, family planning, because we don't have a model family planning program in the United States.

We must develop a model family planning program in the United States which will not directly solve India's problem any more than giving birth control devices to Pakistan is going to solve their problem. One of the problems is that we are giving only birth control devices because we don't understand family planning. We don't understand that we have to prevent the haphazard conception that occurs as the result of sexual encounters that have nothing to do with the planning of children, or the inviting of children into our world - because unfortunately we have never thought about the child and that aspect of maximizing the child's growth and development as the major emphasis, in our confused pattern of living, our confused pattern of relationships. That doesn't mean that we can't begin to do it. It doesn't mean we could not begin to have multiple comprehensive family planning programs in the United States, and we really must - very soon.

DR. STOREY:

Amen.

DR. ABRAHAMSON:

Amen is right. The pollution problem would not be solved were population growth to end today. If we could suddenly stop all population growth, we would still have the pollution problem that we have now. We don't solve the pollution problem by attacking the population problem. We can keep it from getting worse perhaps, but we are not going to solve it. We are still going to have to deal with the problem that we have right now - today - and I think evidence is very strong that even with the pollution control measures that are in effect now, we are still losing ground.

DR. THOMAS VAN KOEVERING (UWGB):

I am wondering if part of this problem where you were talking about people throwing rocks at signs advertising birth control in Pakistan doesn't get back to the philosophy that, at least up until now, there has always been the advantage of sheer number. If we have birth control in Pakistan, then it looks as though they are being put in a situation of disadvantage. I think this is also true in some of the problems in Northern Ireland. I am also thinking of something about which I just read, which was also surprising to me at least. This is the fact that there is a sort of national philosophy in France to try to increase their population. It seems as though in a pretty well developed country, that they could see an advantage to limiting their population because they have a limited amount of land, but their population is somewhere around 50 million people, and as I understand it, they are trying to promote their population to around 100 million people. This is becoming sort of a national trend - advertising the advantages of larger families, etc. I am wondering if it isn't just this sort of thing that we have to attack as well as, perhaps through some educational form, showing that we are running out of the advantage when we have a large group of people.

DR. TAEUBER:

The earliest declines in birth rate in the Western World were in France and Colonial New England. The problem of France insofar as numbers are concerned is to maintain a birth rate high enough that the population does not decline. Before the Second World War, the intrinsic rates of reproduction were not sufficient to maintain the numbers of Frenchmen. Growth involved the importation of Polish labor. At the present time, reproduction of the French population is just about at unity; problems are a totally different thing in a France that has a birth rate of around 18 and a Pakistan that has a birth rate close to 50.

There is another hazard in the associations of government and birth control. If there is birth control programs by a government and it is a pushing program, effectively implemented and reaching to local levels, and including major communications with the people, then that program is viewed by the people as a part of the government. If the government then becomes widely questioned by the people and moves into conflict, then birth control which was a program of government may be subject to onslaught. In Pakistan, the new government has the same assessment of the absolute necessity of reducing birth rates in Pakistan that the previous government had. The program continues to function.

MR. GREENWOOD:

Our course at UWGB last semester was a survey program of what we have been talking about. We had different speakers come in and we discussed many of the problems that we have been talking about today. Oddly enough, it seems the same thing happened there that seems to be happening here. We started with one problem, worked for a solution and we just kept going in circles. We stumbled on to what we thought were the major problems. Number one - possibly not pollution, not population, but lack of communication. We felt that if we could tear down the barrier of communication between countries and get at the apathetic people who seem to look at everything through their own experience, something might be accomplished. If you don't have the experience of an Indian person starving to death and you see a newsreel, you say "that's too bad, 50,000 people died today". We had no experience with this and the majority of us came out with the feeling that we were looking at these people and we just didn't understand. You want to do something about it, but you have to talk through the government perhaps, and if you talk through your government and try to get other governments together, it's impossible. If you are from the United States they don't want to talk to you because you are governmentalized because you have to go through those channels. We just ended up in a dead alley and it seemed pessimistic to conclude that there was no solution. We always discussed the possibility of a world government being a start. It's a "brave new world" idea, but that's about all we could come up with, It may sound kind of Alice in Wonderland type. As far as making them happen, the lack of communication and the breaking of barriers between our people and getting at the apathy is the real need. The other big item is the almighty dollar. Nobody wants to spend it to get what we need. Everybody wants to talk about it, but nobody wants to spend the money to do it. These are the things that we have been thinking about. I am interested to see that we were running somewhat along the same lines as the participants are here.

DR. GYORGY:

You asked Dave Greenwood or a member of the panel a question. This morning, I don't know whether you heard my talk, I expressed great sympathy for the idealism of the "militant" students. I expressed the hope that there would be really an extremely good source of help. I called them volunteers; I should probably call them missionaries in community development in the United States, especially in communities inhabited by underprivileged people. I would like to ask him what is his opinion on this problem, and what does he think would be the opinion of his young colleagues?

MR. GREENWOOD:

I can give you a solution, if you want to call it that. As students in our project in this class, we had to try to solve the problem. Strangely enough, the program you mentioned this morning whereby you spend a certain amount of time as a substitution for military service, we developed also in our discussion. What we did was we have the United Nations as the head, the center, the organization. We take the engineers, chemists, everybody that could help the country, who normally have to serve in the armed forces, and ask them to serve their country for two years in their field in their country, doing their thing, helping their country develop. We would have this supported in the countries that are in need right now of food, or whatever, by the United Nations Food Fleet which would keep these countries going until they could get on their own feet. Therefore, we have people of the nationality working in their country, doing things for their country, supervised - not really supervised but in conjunction with an establishment made up of all of the nations of the world.

The only thing that we found out about this - we had some people say what if a person doesn't want to give up two years of his life - he's an engineer and he's making too much money - right away the big dollar sign rang up. Of course, the cost of the program is vast. I have even been called a dreamer for suggesting it, but it didn't bother me. I am not saying that this is a solution. I am saying that possibly on this order there are so many different things we could do. This is what we came up with and as I said with lack of communication, the money, and with the apathy - we tore our own solution apart and made it almost improbable. I am optimistic myself and that's why I stated something like this along with my fellow classmates. I feel that sooner or later the sensible people of the world are going to have to wake up.

DR. GYORGY:

I am afraid we don't see eye to eye, or I didn't express myself clearly. I don't need expertise - not young experts. I need compassionate, dedicated young people, perhaps finished with their college or even high school. They are idealists and our country needs idealism in their youth.

MR. GREENWOOD:

I realize what you are asking and I would like to answer that as straight as I can by saying that of the students that I have met - first of all if they had a choice of military service or something on the order that you are proposing, there would hardly be any choice. I would say that they would jump at your chance - perhaps some of them through fear of physical harm. There are a lot of students, I believe that would be willing to dedicate two years, if not more, to what you suggest.

I think there are people here who would like to get out and do something for these people. I think that's part of the student's problem. We can talk - sometimes nobody listens - we get a little bit uppity and then everybody listens, and when you have the attention you want to say something, maybe it gets out of hand. You get sidetracked or something. A program like this will give the students the opportunity to express their loyalties to the people of America and to themselves in creating a better world.

DR. GYORGY:

That sounds better.

BONNIE DORN (UWGB):

I find myself feeling perhaps a little bit pessimistic, so I will direct this question to the optimists on the panel. I am also feeling a little frustrated because I am a student and very much in the position of wanting to learn, and of wanting to see what I can do; and I have some ideas on what I would like to do with these problems. I am seeing "experts" who are posing a lot of possibilities, but they all seem to be so deeply involved with our political structure which, as we all know, moves so slowly, and is involved with our economics. Speaking of Madison Avenue, how many people are going to buy snowmobiles this year? It is a vicious circle as Dave mentioned.

I am finding myself a little bit frustrated with the knowledge I have of what excess population can do and the knowledge I have of how many years it takes to do it. I am wondering if we will in time be doing something. At this late stage we are finally talking about it. Oh goody, goody! How long is it going to take before we actually do something? I feel very small and very, very unimportant when I face our political system, our economic system, our struggling U.N. When you talk about world power it seems very much "Cinderella Land" to me - a beautiful dream but are we going to be around? Please somebody comment on this!

DR. STOREY:

I would like to try. All that I can say is that I am as frustrated as you are. I think most of us in this room are as frustrated as you are. I want to urge you to hold on to that frustration and keep working at it because if you have been frustrated for 2 or 3 years, perhaps we have been frustrated for 30 or 40, r 50, and we do make progress. I think I have seen a great deal of it and I think the only way we make progress is because somebody gets frustrated and wants to do something. I have no simple answer for you. Just keep working at it, but don't give up because you are frustrated.

DR. GYORGY:

I have to answer it as an optimist. I don't want to encourage you to remain frustrated. I am sorry. Frustration is not a pleasant state of mind. I would like to bring you an example which made me very happy, and if I ever would have been frustrated than I would have been hyper-active afterwards. In Northeast Thailand, 100% of the population is infested with liver fluke, which is a disease of the liver - parasites nesting in the liver - and there is no drug against it. The liver fluke is ingested with a small fish of the rice paddies, which is first put in an earthware container filled with salt water. It digests itself and often becomes spoiled, but they like the smell of it and the taste of it. They take a little of the sauce and put it on the rice, and this food is then full of the liver fluke. That has been going on for many, many generations - hundreds of generations. My recommendation was to take students of Ceng Mai University in North Thailand and it happened that there were some just graduated with a B.A. in psychology, and six of them were sent to six villages. They had all the ecological recommendations from me and my associates. I have not been there, but have been working in the background. One of my recommendations has been to persuade the people to boil the fermented fish sauce before they use it. Everybody was laughing at me - Thais; in Laos it was the same story - in Laos they were laughing at me. They said it was impossible. They said people would not do it because boiling would change the taste that they are accustomed to. Three months later when I came back from Laos to Bangkok, my associate from Northeast Thailand came down and congratulated me. Like a wildfire, from one village to the other village, it spreads "you have to boil because then you save your life", and they have been boiling the fermented fish "soup" since September. Thus, these communities of underprivileged people achieved in a very short period of time improvement; maybe of not such a dramatic import, but still - there was nothing needed except a sympathetic "missionary" who persuaded the people to boil the fermented fish sauce. And that was the end of it. Now the children who are born, or who are already growing up, will not get the disease anymore and will not be infested. They will not be sick, nor weak and will have a happier life.

DR. STOREY:

I have to try again because I can't agree with Dr. Gyorgy that we should give up frustration, because when we are frustrated we care. When we care, we are not being apathetic and we are not at the end of the seven stages of man that I talked about. If you can combine your frustration with courage, which is one of the early parts of the seven stages of man, then I think you can do something. I am optimistic because you are frustrated.

DR. ABRAHAMSON:

I would like to add one more thing - combine it with knowledge, if you can arrange that. A missionary without knowledge can cause all kinds of trouble. We have abundant evidence of that too.

DR. EUGENE ROBKIN (UWGB):

At the recent annual meeting of the AAAS, Dr. Tamplin presented some results about the effects on babies who were radiated in the womb and born to mothers themselves who were radiated in the womb. It is rather frightening to me that the death rate was so high. I was wondering if Dr. Abrahamson would comment on those results and perhaps couple them with his earlier remarks about the increase in DDT, lead, and mercury and perhaps such things as 2-4-5 T in the environment.

DR. ABRAHAMSON:

If my memory serves me correctly, you are referring to a study done at Johns Hopkins School of Medicine by Meyer, Merz and Diamond. (Reported in the American Journal of Epidemiology in 1969 - volume 89, number 6, pages 619 through 635) Several years ago, it was much more common than it is today to give pelvic x-rays to pregnant women. In this study a number of women whose mothers had received x-rays while they were being carried were investigated. The women being studied were pregnant and did not receive radiation. There was an abnormally large number of male children born of these women compared to the number of female children. In other words, mothers, who had themselves been irradiated during the time that their mothers were pregnant with them, produced an unusually high number of male children. If this is a valid observation, and I know of no reason why it should be questioned, it strongly suggests that the effects from levels of ionizing radiation which are presently allowed under statute may have substantial effects.

To even begin an answer to your second question would take more time than we have available. It should be obvious, however, that the fact that we have been careless with, for example, DDT does not justify being careless with radiation.

MR. GARY HOTCHKIN (University of Hawaii):

We have been talking today about overpopulation and I think we all seem to sense that it is a problem. I would agree that before we start telling anybody else how to do anything about it, that we have got to do something about it ourselves. I think then, and I am posing this more as a question, is it not our task to make the other population, or overpopulation areas, realize that it is a problem, for them to take up rather than for us to help them do something about it? I think this is all too often how we acquire the "ugly American" image. We can't go in and impose upon them the fact that they are overpopulated and should observe birth control because we say it's good. Is it not our objective to help them realize that it would be beneficial to them?

DR. TAEUBER:

There have been swift developments in population fields in recent years, however adequate or inadequate they may be. The United Nations organizations are all involved. There is a Population Division in the central secretariat in New York. There is a Population Commissioner in the development fund. FAO, WHO, Unesco, ILO, are involved. There is a coordinating committee that meets regularly in Geneva for the United Nations system. There are also the regional organizations such as OAS, Pan American Health Organization, Colombo Plan. The United States is involved officially and through private groups. The verbal position is that help is given in response to requests from countries, in cooperation with them, and as contributions to them. There are involvements of news and other media. The Mainichi Press in Japan has carried population as major news for a long time.

While I have the floor, I would like to say one thing that I debated putting in a while ago, and did not. In the discussion of relations of governments, there are stories of "Ugly Americans" in population fields. But as scientists and scholars, we have no problems of full, open and cooperative relations with our colleagues in any country in the world. Have you had any?

DR. GYORGY:

Not with your colleagues, no.

DR. TAEUBER:

If you have bright ideas for research that should be done within other countries, give them to your colleagues.

DR. GYORGY:

I know "Ugly Americans" - experts who created havoc by their behavior among their national collaborators. These colleagues, and it happened they were young ladies - doctors - they came to me and they were crying in defense of their approach. You have to be diplomatic.

DR. TAEUBER:

In talking or appealing to students to move into these areas, the approaches must be explained explicitly. If you are humanitarian and humble, people will sort of guide you gently and teach you how to move. If you have competence and identification with humanity, and a middle amount - not too much - of humility, you can find your task and secure cooperation in it.

DR. DOBERENZ:

Regrettably, I will have to terminate this panel - we could go on for at least another two hours, but it is getting late. I want to thank all of the panel members and all of the members of the audience too for without you and your questions, we could not have developed this dialog. I hope that this will continue on into tomorrow's program.

I would like to remind you that tomorrow's program will take place at the UWGB Campus in the main lecture hall in the Environmental Sciences Building. We start at 9 o'clock. Also, at 5:30 this evening here, directly outside in the lobby, we will have a reception at which time I would assume that you will have a chance to chat with any of the speakers and ask additional questions. I would also like to remind you that Mr. Robert McLaughlin will be speaking this evening at the dinner, and his talk will be "Fertility Reduction: Can Voluntary Approaches Succeed".

EVENING DINNER SESSION
9 January

Chairman - Dr. Frank Byrne
          Secretary of the Faculty
          University of Wisconsin - Green Bay

Dr. Byrne: On behalf of the students, staff, and faculty, I bid you welcome to the University of Wisconsin - Green Bay. We are so very pleased that you could be with us for the introduction of the academic program in the College of Human Biology, one of the four theme colleges around which the University is built.

When Dean Beaton asked me to serve in the role I have, I wondered how appropriate I would be to it - by profession, I am a geologist. Dean Beaton explained it very simply this way. A symposium titled as ours is, Population Growth, depends on babies to accomplish that growth in the population. Babies require cradles, of course. And there must needs be someone to rock the cradles. Hence my appropriateness, as a geologist, to the program.

In such a meeting as this, there is a lot of planning that goes on, but there is a lot of work not so easily seen as a result of the planning. Much of that work is done by people who are here, and we have two of them tonight. So to their flustered surprise, I would like to introduce two people so very, very instrumental in making this the success that it is - the secretary of the College of Human Biology, Mrs. Jo Berentson, and Jo's very good, and very pretty, right hand, Joan Carpiaux.

I would like too to acknowledge the guests who have contributed so generously of their talents, the results of their personal interests, and the researches that they have conducted. Those you have heard speak this morning, this afternoon, and you will hear some more of their discussions tomorrow morning.

At the head table, we have Mrs. Doris Byrne, Mrs. Jean Weidner, Dr. John Beaton, Dean of the College of Human Biology; Mr. Robert McLaughlin of the Ford Foundation in New York; our Chancellor, Dr. Edward W. Weidner; Mrs. Helen Beaton, and me.

To introduce our speaker, we have, very pleasurably, Dr. Edward W. Weidner, Chancellor of the University of Wisconsin - Green Bay.

Introduction of Mr. Robert T. McLaughlin
Edward W. Weidner

Here is a quotation that I thought was particularly appropriate for our discussions concerning the University of Wisconsin - Green Bay and what we are trying to do. "Everyone knows that the departmentalizing of American education, so efficient in appearance, is often deadly in fact. The life of man and the nature of civilization are wholes, not arrangements of hermetically sealed compartments. The student often forgets that the world the philosophers think about, and the world the physicists measure, are the same world and education is not designed to teach him subjects, but to orient him in civilization". This could be a preface to our Academic Plan. Still, it appeared in the New York Herald Tribune in the year 1927. It referred to the experimental college of the University of Wisconsin in Madison, long since gone. We are inheritors of a proud tradition.

We turn this evening to a talk on population and the problem of population control. A baby arrives every 12 seconds in the United States, but we get a car every 5 seconds, and there is an interesting connection there. Between the two of them about 2 acres of countryside is taken up every minute. So, I don't mean to align myself with the pessimists that were holding forth this afternoon, nor with the optimists. But we have a severe problem.

The speaker this evening has packed into relatively few years a very exciting career - a career that has taken him more than once to Latin America; a career that has taken him overseas in connection with the Peace Corps, with AID, and the Ford Foundation; and think what a wonderful set of hypotheses he could come forward with if he reflected upon his own personal experiences with these three organizations! We all know that some of these agencies tend to have less happy public relations abroad than others. He was in Peru with the Peace Corps. He was stationed next to the Pacific Ocean for one assignment and went up into the mountains with the Indians for another. He was later with AID in Colombia. He has an impeccable pedigree, Harvard and Princeton. There is no question as to why he ended up in the Ford Foundation with that background. He is currently working on population problems in the International Division of the Ford Foundation.

It gives me great pleasure to introduce Mr. Robert McLaughlin.

student often forgets that the world the philosophers think about, and the world the physicists measure, are the same world and education is not designed to teach him subjects, but to orient him in civilization." This could be a preface to our Academic Plan. Still, it appeared in the New York Herald Tribune in the year 1927. It referred to the experimental college of the University of Wisconsin in Madison, long since gone. We are inheritors of a proud tradition.

We turn this evening to a talk on population and the problem of population control. A baby arrives every 12 seconds in the United States, but we get a car every 5 seconds, and there is an interesting connection there. Between the two of them about 2 acres of countryside is taken up every minute. So, I don't mean to align myself with the pessimists that were holding forth this afternoon, nor with the optimists. But we have a severe problem.

The speaker this evening has packed into relatively few years a very exciting career — a career that has taken him more than once to Latin America; a career that has taken him overseas in connection with the Peace Corps, with AID, and the Ford Foundation; and think what a wonderful set of hypotheses he could come forward with if he reflected upon his own personal experiences with these three organizations! We all know that some of these agencies tend to have less happy public relations abroad than others. He was in Peru with the Peace Corps. He was stationed next to the Pacific Ocean for one assignment and went up into the mountains with the Indians for another. He was later with AID in Colombia. He has an impeccable pedigree, Harvard and Princeton. There is no question as to why he ended up in the Ford Foundation with that background. He is currently working on population problems in the International Division of the Ford Foundation.

It gives me great pleasure to introduce Mr. Robert McLaughlin.

Fertility Reduction:
Can Voluntary Approaches Succeed

ROBERT T. McLAUGHLIN

Office of Population,
Ford Foundation

Let me begin by telling you which approaches to fertility reduction I am calling voluntary, and which ones seem to me to go beyond that concept. In general, the voluntary approaches are summarized in the traditional motto of FP organizations: "every child a wanted child". In other words, they leave all choices about how many children and how they are to be spaced entirely up to individual couples.

One assumption lying beneath these approaches is that a substantial portion of the world's population growth is presently accounted for by "excess fertility" - - undesired and unplanned births.

This is the rationale which supports voluntary family planning programs around the world, whether sponsored by private or public agencies.

There are currently some 25 countries in the developing world which have officially committed themselves to a national family planning program. They range all the way from India, whose government-supported program has been underway for 18 years, to Ghana, where a small-scale effort has just begun.

The typical sequence by which a developing country hesitantly launches a national family planning program has been well described by the President of the Population Council, Bernard Berelson:

"The pressure for family planning policy typically originates in the planning board or its equivalent, as economists come to appreciate what the current rate of population growth means for their development plans - or, in fewer countries, it originates in medical circles with concern over the high incidence of induced abortions and their personal and social costs. (The ground has often been prepared by the local private family planning association; and its relationship to the governmental effort sometimes makes for the natural tensions of organizational rivalries.) Someone in a high position who wishes to promote the policy invites a foreign mission of experts to review the population situation and make recommendations which then call for adoption of a family planning policy. Even after the policy is formally proclaimed, however, there often remains some ambivalence at high levels based on political sensitivities, actual or perceived.

When the effort does begin it is placed under medical auspices: the official program becomes the responsibility of the Ministry of Health, it is closely tied to maternal and child health services and health centers, and a medical man with experience in public health is usually named director of the programs. He begins by designating family planning as another health service, to be administered through the existing network, and/or by setting up family planning clinics wherever possible. These approaches typically fail and slowly the responsible officials (who by now are likely not to be the ones who started in charge) come to recognize that more vigorous efforts are needed in the form of special staff, materials, and supplies, and in ways to reach people rather than waiting for them to come in.

Meanwhile, the medical people are reviewing available contraceptive methods and doing clinical tests to see which will be approved for use in their country; communications specialists are only slowly developing informational and educational materials and campaigns, partly because of some reluctance at high levels to allow full publicity; and the bureaucracy - particularly finance, and, where they exist, relations between the central and regional government units - takes its inevitable toll.

Sooner or later, information, services and supplies are brought to the attention of the target population, usually through female field workers specially trained for the purpose; and contraceptive methods are offered free of charge on a voluntary basis and as a so-called cafeteria choice of techniques, though with particular emphasis on the IUD as presumably the most effective method. Incentive payments for medical and paramedical personnel are provided and often finder's fees as well - for which a rather elaborate scheme for administration needs to be developed. An evaluation unit is set up to guide the program and measure its results, and it does either job only with some difficulty and delay. Throughout this period the program has received external assistance in both funding and expertise. By this time, it is a few years after the policy decision was taken, an organization to do the work is just coming into effective operation, and any effect on the birth rate is yet to be demonstrated if not actually brought about."

Notice that this typical family planning program described by Dr. Berelson does <u>not</u> involve fundamental shifts of the social or economic environment to reward small families or penalize large ones. The publicity campaigns and small inducements may slightly load the dice in favor of family planning, but they do not change the rules of the game.

Now, as you know, there are a number of qualified observers who dismiss the approaches I have outlined as wholly inadequate to the task at hand. I will mention just a few examples. On a theoretical level, Garrett Hardin has stated his belief that only "mutual coercion, mutually agreed upon" will curb man's hereditary urge to produce large families, and that appeals to responsibility or conscience will prove fruitless because in the long run those people who do respond to the appeals will simply breed themselves out of existence.

84

On a programatic level, Kingsley Davis has concluded that national FP programs around the world will have at best marginal effects, and that the existing pronatalist "social structure and economy must be changed before a deliberate reduction in the birth rate can be achieved". More recently, Judith Blake Davis has charged that the domestic family planning programs now financed by the Federal Government are unnecessary, undesired and destined to have little or no effect on U.S. population growth. She concludes that a reduction in the U.S. growth rate will require basic changes in the social organization of reproduction that will make non-marriage, childlessness, and small (two child) families far more prevalent than they are now".

With this background, I would like to mention some of the proposals which have been made for measures above and beyond current fertility reduction programs. They range from simple extensions and modifications of the present voluntary programs to radical and frankly coercive schemes. I will draw heavily from Dr. Berelson's analysis of these measures in his article entitled "Beyond Family Planning".

At the mild end of the spectrum are proposals for instituting complete maternal and infant health programs in the rural areas of developing countries. Such programs would, of course, include family planning services, and the lowering of infant mortality would allow couples to achieve their desired family size with fewer births. Another often proposed modification to present programs would be to offer abortion as a backup for failed contraception. Still another is the encouragement of commercial distribution and advertising of non-prescription contraceptives, or the relaxing of medical regulations which apply to the prescription methods.

There have been many proposals about educational and publicity campaigns. It has been suggested that every school child should be taught about the world's population problem, and also informed about family planning. Satellite Television systems offer a promising vehicle for information about family planning, and such a system will soon be available in India. In the meantime, there are many nations which have only timidly begun to use their existing communications media for these messages.

Next we come to the category of proposals usually called "Incentive Programs". These involve direct payments, in money or goods, to couples who practice contraception. In some versions, the payment would be made at the moment that contraception was first accepted. A leading Indian official has proposed that transistor radios be offered for male sterilization, and several countries offer small payments to cover the "lost time" of those who come to family planning clinics. It has also been proposed that payments be offered for periods of non-pregnancy or non-birth: either a small payment (no baby bonus) for short periods, or a long range savings plan or "family planning bond" for longer periods.

Aside from these "positive incentives", there have been proposals for tax or social service modifications which would make large families less attractive. In fact, there are almost endless varieties of these: tax

85

schedules could be revised to favor small families and single people. Births beyond a certain number could be taxed. Schooling could be restricted to only a certain number of children per family.

Other proposals have been made relating to shifts in fundamental social and economic institutions. An increase in the minimum age of marriage is often mentioned, or the promotion of greater female participation in the labor force. It has been suggested that 2 types of marriage be established - one of them childless and easily dissolved.

Finally, there have been proposals for direct government controls over fertility. Some have suggested that a fertility control agent could be added to water supplies or staple food, with the antidote for sale by the government or available by lottery. Others have suggested government issued licenses to have children.

In short, it is a broad spectrum, and there have been many proposals. In fact, some of these ideas have existed in some form for many years.

I don't think it will come as a surprise to you when I say that aside from the mild proposals, <u>there haven't been many takers</u>. No substantial <u>positive</u> incentive scheme has yet been tried, although it is possible that one will be in the next few years. The same goes for the negative incentives. Virtually all governments continue to offer welfare benefits and tax relief to large families. Only one state government in India has ever endorsed governmental control of family size, and it is far from certain that the idea will be implemented.

Why have so many nations adopted essentially similar approaches to fertility reduction, and why have they shunned the more forceful measures which I have mentioned? It may sound like dangerous ignorance or wilfull neglect in the face of a grave threat, but I think that the reasons are not hard to understand. They go far toward answering the question I posed in the title of this talk.

In the first place, leaders in most countries have been slow to discard the traditional reasoning which equated population size and growth with national power and prestige, and they have been slow to believe that efforts to reduce population growth would not cause a storm of political or religious protest in their countries.

Indeed, as Oscar Harkavy has noted: "It requires unusual statesmanship for politicians to become identified with birth control. Beneficial effects of fertility reduction can be realized only in the long run; politicians are necessarily concerned with their careers in the short run. there is little political mileage to be gained from impressive statistics on IUD insertions or cycles of pills distributed, while deleterious side effects of these methods may backfire on those who promote them, and affect their chances of re-election". We in the United States know this story all too well.

In short, we have not yet managed to convince all of our colleagues around the world that present rates of population growth require immediate concern and action. Undoubtedly, our efforts are complicated by the fact that while the developed countries are now allocating substantial funds for world wide family planning programs, funds for other aspects of development are pitifully low, and falling. This leads to the suspicion that the developed nations have simply decided upon birth control as the cheap way out. In any event, it is futile to debate different approaches to the reduction of fertility until we have convinced leaders in all parts of the world that population growth demands their attention.

Given the ambivalence of the world leaders about the severity of the population problem, and their fears of political, cultural, or religious reactions, it is not surprising that they decide to begin their efforts with a low-key, medically conservative, and entirely voluntary program.

Such a program, after all, is a natural extension of the democratic philosophical principals which almost all of these nations profess to hold dear, and as such is likely to provoke the least opposition. It is highly unlikely that any government would adopt more forceful measures before the milder ones had been fully tested.

It is tempting to say that the mild measures have been fully tested, and found wanting. After all, India has supported some kind of family planning program since 1952, and as we all know, a significant decline in the birth rate there has yet to be demonstrated.

I do not agree with that assessment. I think rather that the case of India is one of too little effort and imagination, too little political will, too little foreign assistance, and all of these factors too late.

We often forget that serious efforts in this field date back only 5 or 6 years. Serious money in this field is even more recent!

Another obstacle to progress has surely been the state of contraceptive technology. This may sound like an unfair complaint after a period which has seen the introduction of oral contraceptives and the introuterine device. But both the IUD and the pill leave much to be desired as the basis for birth control in poor countries: both require considerable medical supervision at the outset, and periodic checkups later. Both have side effects which limit their acceptability for some women. Both are far short of the "ideal contraceptive" and we are convinced that improved contraceptive technology will result in much more effective family planning programs, by appealing to couples at successively lower levels of motivation. In addition to these factors, it is now clear that family planning programs have not begun to tap the motivational resources of education and the mass media.

In view of the recent establishment of national family planning programs, and the limitations to which they have been subject, the surprising fact is that in a few places such programs already have had an impact on birth rates. This is surely another reason why nations are attracted to these programs, and why they have thus far shunned the stronger measures.

In Taiwan, the rate of natural increase was about 3% in 1963, at the start of their family planning program, and had declined to 2.4% by the end of 1968. Of course, in a rapidly developing society not all of that decline can be attributed to the program itself, but there is general agreement that the program caused a substantial increase in the rate of decline. South Korea appears to have experienced a similar decline over the same period, although the vital statistics are not as reliable as those of Taiwan. Two other countries which have achieved some success are Hong Kong and Singapore. Are these special cases? Skeptics point out that they are all Asian, small, and on the road toward development. However, they are also the only countries where expenditures on FP have been substantially relative to the population. Only in these countries have 20 - 30% of eligible couples been reached by FP programs. In India and Pakistan, by contrast, the percentage of eligible couples reached is far less.

In Louisiana, to cite a case that is closer to home, a pilot family planning program for the medically indigent was started from scratch in one county in 1965, and two years later the decline in indigent births was five times as great as in control counties. The program has since been expanded to cover the entire state, and similar results are expected.

The lesson of these examples is that well financed and administered family planning programs can have an impact on birth rates. Whether they can lower birth rates to population stabilization levels, we don't yet know. However, even the small successes registered thus far are enough to make me suspect that a vigorous but voluntary program could short circuit the traditional links between fertility and the level of economic development, and bring low fertility to populations that have not yet entered the industrial age in other respects.

If the voluntary approaches still hold out some hope, what are the prospects for some of the other measures I cited? Let us suppose that political and cultural factors will in the short run rule out direct government controls, basic shifts of social structure, and negative incentives. We are left with the positive incentive schemes.

While it is fair to assume that every couple has its price, even with regard to changes in desired family size, the fact of the matter is that we have no idea how high the rewards would have to be. Most European countries during the 30's and 40's experimented with pro-natalist family allowance programs; but there was no evidence that these programs in fact raised birth rates.

Aside from the possibly high expense of a positive incentive program, there is the matter of administration. Typically, countries with high birth rates are not apt to have a great supply of administrative talent. Most of them do not do a good job of gathering simple vital statistics, and the administration of a complicated and corruption-prone scheme such as this one would prove challenging, to say the least.

Nevertheless, I think it is likely that at least a small experiment with positive incentives will be launched somewhere in the next few years. One possible form would be an old age pension plan limited to couples with small families at the end of their reproductive years. Even this approach would not be without its pitfalls, however, as pointed out by Joseph Spengler:

"The weaknesses in these arrangements are three. First, among those whose discount of the future is very high, future monetary rewards may offer only limited incentive in the present when decisions respecting reproduction must be made. Second, confidence in the governmental apparatus of the state may be limited. It may be feared that when rewards come due 20 to 45 years hence, the state will refuse to pay or pay in full. A combination of this fear with a high discount rate could, therefore, greatly reduce the capacity of the joint incentives to diminish fertility. Finally, the arrangements cannot succeed unless the means to control family size are widely available and very cheap in relation to the incomes of the masses."

Spengler's last point should be carefully noted: the existence of modern birth control services will be a vital prerequisite for any anti-natalist social or economic programs that may be adopted by nations in the future.

In summing up, I believe there are compelling reasons for vigorously pursuing the voluntary approaches towards fertility reduction. First because they are the approaches most in agreement with our philosophical and political traditions. Second because there is no country which has yet implemented the full range of these approaches, but there are several which have gone part way and they have achieved partial success. Third because the administrative and political feasibility of more forceful measures is doubtful in most countries. And finally because the services established by the voluntary approaches will be necessary elements of any future approaches.

GENERAL READING SOURCES

1. Beyond Family Planning - Bernard Berelson

2. National Family Planning Programs: Where We Stand -
Bernard Berelson

3. Ford Foundation Strategy for Population Work

4. Family Planning Programs: Is the Government Being Misled? -
Judith Blake Davis

5. Family Planning Programs: Who is Misleading Whom? -
Fred Jaffe, Samuel Wishik, Oscar Harkavy

6. Bibliography - James Bausch

Response to Mr. McLaughlin's Dinner Talk
John R. Beaton

In thanking Robert McLaughlin, I cannot pass up this opportunity to ask a question. Being born and raised in the City of Oshawa, Ontario, I had the very good fortune to know quite well Mr. R. "Sam" McLaughlin, President and Chairman of the Board, General Motors of Canada. Is Robert McLaughlin, here this evening, a relative of "Sam" McLaughlin, who chose Henry Ford as his idol?

On a more serious note, the Ford Foundation has done much to benefit mankind in many small and in very large ways. We are pleased indeed that the Ford Foundation has seen fit to participate in this Symposium through an excellent representative - Robert McLaughlin.

To say that we have benefitted from, and enjoyed, your talk this evening would be an understatement. You have brought to us some thought-provoking concepts which, I am sure, will be carried into tomorrow's session.

We have followed the philosophy that if you ask a good man to do one job, you can hope for more. I don't think Mr. McLaughlin knew that he would be expected to serve also on tomorrow morning's Panel. At this point in time, I wish to announce to Robert McLaughlin that we look forward to asking questions tomorrow - although we do not expect that he will have all of the answers.

In closing, Bob, thank you very much for your excellent address and I hope you will forgive us for our presumption in appointing you to our Panel tomorrow morning. If you can think of a tactful way to avoid this, I would be glad to hear it - even though it won't be accepted.

MORNING SESSION

10 January

Chairman - Dr. William Kaufman
            Chairman, Concentration in Human Adaptability
            University of Wisconsin - Green Bay

Introduction of Dr. Jerry W. Combs, Jr.
William Kaufman

In the 16th century Marlowe's shepherd addressed his lady:

> Come live with me and be my love,
> And we will all the pleasures prove,
> That valleys, groves, hills and fields,
> Woods or steepy mountain yields.

That sort of ardor, coupled with the great capabilities of his mind, have made man the most successful of all animal populations; his numbers have multiplied at an ever-increasing rate. Mankind is also the most successful decimator of wild populations and the greatest producer of waste.

The shepherd of the future may not be able to find an untenanted valley, grove, hill, or field, and may view only algae-filled bogs or great heaps of empty bottles, cans and junked auto bodies under a permanently hazy sky. He might converse with his lady, in something less than Elizabethan poetry, thus:

> Love is fine, sex is great,
> Gee, it's fun to procreate.
> But, darling, zooming population,
> Raises hell with recreation.
> Lakes are cloudy, sky is dim,
> Damn, there is no place to swim
> Great thing, my dear, that I have you
> Now there's nothing else to do.

Population conferences are not unique. In 1753, Robert Wallace published his "Dissertation on the Numbers of Mankind", and stated before the Philosophical Society that humble virtues were "consistent with" and "greatly conducive to the populousness and grandeur of society". A few years later Malthus was suggesting prudent restraint to population growth. More recently, in 1928, Aldous Huxley had his nobleman biologist, decrying the loss of phosphates from farm fields into the Thames and remarking that he would welcome a social revolution if it would reduce the population.

A population conference in Green Bay, in Northeastern Wisconsin, where the countryside is still to a large extent uncluttered and the sky relatively clear might be considered unique by the uninformed.

Wisconsin is known for its progressive university and progressive legislators. It led in the recognition of the dangers of pesticides and has recently passed sophisticated drug legislation and reconsidered its laws concerning contraceptives.

About 100 years ago Green Bay was the home of Dr. William Beaumong a pioneer gastroenterologist who did imaginative and learned research in gastric physiology.

Now Green Bay has become the home of a university which has received national publicity for its dedication to the pursuit of solutions to the problems with which man has presented himself through the unrestricted use of natural resources, the over population of the earth and the resulting pollution of his environment.

So it is fitting, in this region with a tradition of progressivism and a history of taking early first steps, that we anticipate and hope-fully forestall one of man's most crucial problems through this Symposium, "Population Growth: Crisis and Challenge.

Our first speaker this morning is Dr. Jerry W. Combs, Jr. He re-ceived his doctorate in sociology at Columbia University, a member of the faculty at Emory University, on the staff of the Air Force Personnel Training Research Laboratory; and he is now the Chief of the Behavioral Sciences Branch in the Center for Population Research, with the U.S. Public Health Service.

His topic is "The Role of the Federal Government in Population Research".

The Role of the Federal Government In Population Research

JERRY W. COMBS, JR., Ph.D.

Chief, Behavioral Sciences Branch,
Center for Population Research,
National Institute of Child Health
and Human Development

The Federal Government has been involved in one aspect or another of population research for a number of years. The many here who have engaged in population research themselves do not need to be reminded of the information gathered over a very long period by the Bureau of the Census, of the fairly long history of vital statistics collection and analysis by the National Center for Health Statistics and its predecessors, the work of the Department of Agriculture on various aspects of the farm population, and of the Department of Labor in the field of manpower. Other agencies have also been involved. All these agencies, however, have treated population data as information to be adapted to, to be used to guide government and the private sector in formulating or administering a variety of programs. They have rarely pursued the study of population with the intent of altering the course of its development. What we shall concentrate upon in this paper, therefore, is not the past contributions of these more traditional data collection and analysis activities, or upon their probably expanded role in the future. Rather, we shall concentrate our attention upon a relatively new endeavor within the Federal Government, that of the Center for Population Research -- an endeavor that is new both in terms of age and of intent. For this Center represents an explicit effort by an agency of the Federal Government to pursue research directed toward the increase in our store of information on the dimensions of population as a problem, and toward the accumulation of knowledge which will increase our capacity to influence the course of population growth and development itself.

In his Health Message of March, 1968, President Johnson called for the establishment of such a Center to pursue research in two fields long neglected: "population and human reproduction". "A wide range of scientists", he said, "must bring to these problems their specialized disciplines -- biologists, behavioral scientists, biochemists, pharmacologists, demographers. experts in population dynamics. . . The Center will serve to give new energy and direction to the research activities of all Federal departments in these fields."

In response to this mandate, the Center for Population Research was established in August 1968, and has undertaken (1) to be the focus of information for the variety of population research efforts by Federal agencies, and (2) to give impetus to an expanded program of population research through the mechanisms of research contracts and grants.

The first of these tasks, that of stimulating population research by the various Federal agencies, has been assumed in the main by the Program Liaison Branch of the Center. It is working to define the field, identify relevant activities throughout the Federal structure, and to work through representatives of the various agencies to encourage their research in the field of population and to coordinate their efforts by maintaining communication among them. The Branch also maintains close liaison with the private and international agencies whose activities are closely related to those of the Center, and is formulating plans for a Population Centers program designed to provide long-range support of selected institutions for education, training, and research in the population field. Announcement of the details of this program will probably be made sometime this year.

The second of the tasks, that of supporting research directly, is accomplished at the present time through three research branches: the Contraceptive Development Branch and the Behavioral Sciences Branch, both of which use the mechanism of contracts to support research, and the Reproduction and Population Grants Branch, which, as its name implies, supports research through the mechanism of research grants. The Grants Program, added to the Center only during the last year, has a much longer prior history within NICHD, especially in the field of basic biological research dealing with reproduction, but its population program in the field of the behavioral and social sciences has been considerably expanded. Although the grants mechanism does not lend itself as clearly to a program of development as is followed under the contract program in the Contraceptive Development Branch, what will be said subsequently about the programs of research formulated under the other two branches is in the main applicable to this Branch also. It does, in addition, make available training grants to educational institutions in all fields related to reproduction and population.

Contraceptive Development

The most highly developed and most clearly focused research effort of the Center at the present time is that carried on through the Contraceptive Development Branch. Under that program, research is directed toward (1) an increased understanding of the fundamental processes of human reproductive biology, (2) the development of new means of fertility control, (3) the study of the medical effects of various contraceptive methods, and (4) the refinement and improvement of presently available methods. In sum, its aim is to develop a variety of contraceptives that are effective, safe, inexpensive, reversible, and acceptable to various population groups under varying conditions. A discussion of the details of the research already under way in these areas is outside the competence of the present speaker. Suffice it to say that the initial phase of this program has been concentrated primarily on fundamental studies in reproductive biology considered to be especially pertinent to fertility control; substantial support is also being directed toward the medical effects of current contraceptives. Literature on the scope of the program in this area is available on request from the Center for Population Research.

Research in the Behavioral and Social Sciences

Equally as important and fundamental to a solution of both the personal and societal problems of population growth as the development of more satisfactory methods of contraception is the development of knowledge about the personal motivations and the social contexts involved in decisions to have or not to have children and in the successful use of known available contraceptives on the part of those who wish to limit their fertility. Beyond that is the need for an increase in the knowledge of how the motivations and contexts may be sufficiently altered to provide desirable rates of population growth within this country and in the world at large.

Research in this area requires, moreover, a far greater expansion of research effort and the involvement of a far larger number of scientists previously uncommitted to the field, than is the case in the biological sciences. In addition, the problems are far less clearly defined, and involve a great many more aspects of human behavior. It may be at some future date that our research will have taught us to specify the problems with utter simplicity and clarity, but we cannot do this today. Instead, we are faced with the problem of inquiring into the complex value systems, social and cultural training, and interfamilial relationships which give rise to fertility norms and fertility behavior, as well as the variety of social, economic, religious, and other influences which impinge upon individuals and determine their demographic behavior. At the same time, if we set our sights too low, and fail to inquire into the consequences of given levels of fertility behavior and of the social mechanisms by which they are determined, we could easily duplicate the follies which have brought us face to face with the various crises of urban growth, environmental pollution, exhaustion of resources, etc., which now occupy so much of the public concern. We must also reckon with the possible transformation of values, economic, political and family structures which may be involved. As population becomes a more and more critical issue, as seems likely, the more profound the research base on which various programs designed to correct the relevant demographic processes, the more adequate and socially beneficial the solutions are going to be. It is a challenge that I hope social scientists across a very broad spectrum will accept and meet - but it is a challenge that requires new foci of interests, new and grander conceptualizations, the critical review of information and theories developed in the past, the possible resurrection and refurbishing of some old, perhaps discarded concepts, the rejection of others, and the disciplined refinement of much in current thought that is vague, irrelevant and unproductive.

The present program of research in the social sciences is accordingly aimed at very broadly based knowledge of the processes of demographic development, of the causes and consequences of population growth, structure, and change, but it places a particular and primary emphasis on fertility.

Currently, the program is organized around four research areas. Though not mutually exclusive, these four areas focus attention upon what we consider major problems. These are designated as follows:

1. Antecedents, processes, and consequences of population structure, distribution, and change.

2. Trends in fertility and related variables.

3. Family structure, sexual behavior, and the relationship between childbearing patterns and child development.

4. Population policies.

We will not go into as great detail here as we have gone in the announcements of our contract program or in the requests for proposals we have issued, but we will attempt to summarize briefly the scope of research we wish to stimulate under each of these headings.

1. Antecedents, processes, and consequences of population structure, distribution, and change.

Under this heading fall a great range of studies dealing with the interrelationships between population and social, economic, political and other changes. The emphasis is both upon the determinants and the consequences of population change. Our interest here is both regional and national, and embraces the interrelationships between all the demographic variables and relevant institutional structures within the society. We are seeking to promote research on the ways in which socio-economic factors affect human behavior related to marriage, fertility, mortality, and migration, and, through these variables, determine the structure and size of populations. We are interested in promoting such studies with reference to subgroups of the population, whether regional or ethnic. We are interested, further, in discovering the basic conditions under which fertility controls will be adopted in specific societies or groups and, if possible, in any society. The relationship between one social variable and another frequently takes place through a chain of circumstances, and the more meaningful studies in this area, we feel, are those which detail the process by which one event influences another. And we are interested in promoting studies dealing with consequences of both fertility trends and migratory patterns, not only in their demographic aspect, but also in their personal and societal aspects.

2. Trends in fertility and related variables.

For several reasons, the crucial questions relating to population growth and change in the modern world ultimately focus on fertility and on the institution of the family within which childbearing and childrearing normally occur. A fundamental concern of the research program of the Center is with the analysis of trends in fertility, in age at marriage, in the incidence of such phenomena as induced abortion and illegitimacy, trends in divorce, etc. We need far more skill in detecting trends, far more information regarding the individual motivations underlying the changes that occur, and the social, economic, political, and other changes which affect them. The Center seeks to promote both the increase in data relevant to these topics and the more extensive analysis of data already available or to become available. It seeks to foster more research in the underlying causes of such trends, the motivations of individuals involved and the social contexts in which the trends occur. In particular, we place emphasis upon the factors which affect decisions relating to having children and the success of couples in carrying out these decisions, and upon the various goals or values which couples perceive as alternatives to childbearing.

3. Family structure, sexual behavior, and the relationship between childbearing patterns and child development.

Since the factors affecting fertility express themselves mainly within the framework of the family, a major area of research must concentrate on behavior of individuals in the family setting, variations in the structure of this institution and changes taking place in it, and the influence of such changes on fertility. More research is needed on the functions of the family within our society, the family kinship networks which exist, and the degree to which traditional family functions relating to childrearing are being supplemented or supplanted by other institutions. More research is needed on the extent to which changes in sexual attitudes and sexual behavior influence age at marriage, age at first conception, divorce, and remarriage. We need, additionally, much more research on the process of socialization for marriage and parenthood, the contributions to this process by the family and other institutions, especially the public and private schools at all age levels, and the contributions to this process by the peer groups in various segments of the population. It should become clear, if you give the matter careful thought, that the interrelationships involved in such studies are unlikely to be unfolded in great depth by survey methods alone, although much research will continue to be done via the survey, but that the findings and observations must be guided, supplemented, and strengthened by considerable insight on the part of researchers whose immersion in the phenomena is comprehensive and profound. Our need for insight is greater than that for tabulations.

In addition, there is considerable need for studies on the relationship between family structure and the emotional development of children, as well as upon the consequences of various childbearing patterns for both the emotional development of the children and the life patterns of the parents themselves. Thoughtful studies in these areas would obviously provide couples with an array of information on which to base their fertility decisions which is lacking to most young couples in our society today.

4. Population policies.

Inevitably, concern with problems of population growth lead to questions of public policy. First, there are questions regarding the effects of current or past public policies upon population change. More work is needed on the evaluation of population policies tried in the past. We also need mechanisms for examining the effects of present Federal and State policies on both population growth and distribution. We know far too little about the demographic implications of economic and investment policies, tax policies, housing and mortgage policies, agricultural subsidies, OEO programs, etc. Government policies with respect to conscription and education, to give but two additional examples, need to be studied in relation to their immediate and long-range effect upon fertility. Another fundamental question relating to policy has to do with the effect of family allowances on fertility. Equally in dispute are the effects of welfare programs of various types, including guaranteed annual income, upon the fertility of the recipient populations.

There is also a wide range of possible studies dealing with family planning programs. The Center for Population Research has avoided an explicit commitment to support studies in this area, because there are a large number of other government agencies which are primarily concerned with the administration of such programs. The evaluation of assumptions on which family programs are organized, however, and the development of measures of effectiveness of such programs, are considered especially relevant to our program, and will be supported.

Finally, it is impossible to avoid some consideration of what a governmental policy in a democratic society should consist of. What are the appropriate concerns of population policy, what should be its goals, and how may its aims be implemented? Needless to say, the appropriate scope of governmental policies is concerned with questions on which little research has been done. These questions have to do with the morality of population increase, the values attached to fertility, and of the relation between the aspirations of people and how these are impeded or promoted by population growth. These questions also have to do with the changing attitudes toward population within various subgroups - politicians, government officials, businessmen, religious and ethnic groups.

To a very large degree, studies in the other areas that have been outlined will provide the raw materials upon which public policies should ultimately be based. But to a large degree also, other studies which are germane to the development of population policies, do not lie within the traditional framework of social science research. They involve questions of the legitimacy of controls (of whatever nature, and whether direct or indirect), the extent as well as the limits of individual rights and freedoms. Before societies can move beyond the current encouragement of individual families to limit their fertility, a considerable amount of thought - social, religious, ethical, and political - is going to have to be brought to bear on the variety of questions raised. At this point, we have not seen our way clearly enough to outline precisely a series of studies in this area but, as in other areas outlined, we invite submission of proposals by qualified individuals.

The foregoing sketches briefly the scope of our current program. As knowledge in these areas accumulates, we shall, of course, alter our emphases and focus more specifically upon detailed projects. We intend to keep our outline of needed and desired research continually under review and to find better ways of communicating those needs to the academic and research community. At the present time we feel that the greatest need is for extensive studies, in depth, of the nexi between the institutional structure and decisions with respect to the timing, spacing, and total number of births. We feel a great inadequacy in our information regarding the socialization process, particularly as it affects size-of-family ideals, and the way in which childbearing is incorporated into the total value system of individuals. We need far more research into the effects of population growth upon a variety of community and national problems, so that the public as well as public opinion leaders and those charged with implementing national policy can do so from a sound base of relevant information. Population is only one of many problems which cry for solution, but it is intimately related to many of those problems, and the more clearly this is perceived, the more intelligently can public policy, at whatever level, be guided.

We see contributions to this enterprise coming not merely from the small coterie of demographers already at work on various aspects of population, but also from representatives of many other disciplines - sociologists, psychologists, anthropologists, economists, political scientists, even philosophers. Demography itself has always been an eclectic discipline, gathering its recruits from a number of other disciplines; and an expanded program of population research will require the enlistment of far more such scientists as well as the expansion of our frame of reference, the development of new concepts, and particularly the clarification of those aspects of population which lend themselves uniquely to study by those not now considered demographers. It is essentially a cooperative enterprise on which we are embarked, and one in which we welcome the participation of the greatest variety of scientists possible.

Current Status of the Program

The Research Program of the Center is, as stated earlier, financed through both grants and contracts. Grant proposals are solicited three times each year through the Division of Research Grants, NIH. Contract proposals are solicited by both the Contraceptive Development and Behavioral Sciences Branches through a formal Request for Proposals which is sent to a select group of institutions who have qualified in terms of interest and capability.

In Fiscal Year 1969, the total funding for research projects through the Center amounted to 8.6 million dollars, of which 3.9 were expended through the grant mechanism for both population and reproductive biology research and 4.8 million through contracts. Of the contract expenditures, 1.2 million went to the study of medical effects of contraceptives, 2.9 million to contraceptive development, and .7 million to population research in the social sciences. In this fiscal year (1970), some increase in these totals are anticipated. Already 1.8 million dollars of contract proposals for contraceptive development have been approved, but not yet funded, and approximately another 1 million of contracts previously approved will be renewed. Renewals under the Social Sciences program will amount to about $500,000 and projects approved and funded will add another $200,000, while projects approved but not yet funded will add an additional 1 million, for a total expected for this year so far of about 1.7 million dollars. Both the Contraceptive Development and Behavioral Sciences Branches intend to review additional proposals in early 1970 for possible funding by July 1. The grants program is continuing at a somewhat increased level for research, and at about the same level as in past years for training.

In addition to the promotion of research through contracts and grants, the Center is seeking to stimulate professional activity relating to population through the sponsorship of conferences. In the last year, the Center has sponsored a "Workshop on Contraceptive Specification", conferences on "Metabolic Effects of Steroid Hormones,", on "Human Sterilization", and on "Abortion". Together with the Fogarty International Center, it has sponsored a conference on "The Family in Transition"; and it will bring together in February a group of about twenty-five participants to deal with the problem of collecting and analyzing migration histories. Others are in the planning stage. Further, it has organized a small "Task Force on the 1970 Census", to focus upon critical research needs which may be met from data being collected in the census to be taken this year.

The program, as it has developed, has relied heavily upon leading scientists in the biological, medical, and social sciences. Following the pattern established within the National Institutes of Health, it has been guided in its development by an Advisory Panel, and makes extensive use of the most prominent scientists in the field. It is, indeed, an extension of the best thought within the scientific community, and its research activities reflect the competent and collective judgment of its review panels, the membership of which is drawn from outside the National Institutes of Health. Under both the Grants and Contract mechanisms, proposals are reviewed by panels of competent scientists from outside NIH, referred to as "Study Sections" under the Grants Program, as "Ad Hoc Review Panels" under the Contracts Program. Thus, all proposals undergo peer review. Funding decisions are made on the basis of the recommendations of these review panels and study sections, within the framework of available appropriated funds. The demands placed upon these outside counsellors is great, and it is to the credit of the various disciplines represented that they have responded with a very great sense of dedication.

We expect that the program of research will continue to expand. As it does so, it is hoped that the Requests for Proposals will become increasingly specific. It has been the philosophy of those advising the program's development, however, that basic research must go hand-in-hand with significant applied or mission-oriented research, and it is our present plan to continue this philosophy.

As I mentioned earlier, the Center is developing plans to further stimulate education, training, and research in the various fields which may make potential contributions to the study of population through a Population Centers Program. The exact form of this program cannot be outlined at the present time. It may be said, however, that it will involve the contribution of funds as core support to a number of institutions to enable them to expand programs of study and training, with a view of expanding the research potential in the various related fields and to stimulating, insofar as possible, multidisciplinary and interdisciplinary efforts in the solution of population problems.

Introduction of Dr. Ronald J. Pion
William Kaufman

Our second speaker is Dr. Ronald J. Pion. He did his medical degree at New York Medical College, his residency in obstetrics and gynecology at the UCLA Medical Center, and studied further at the Karolinska in Stockholm, Sweden.

He is a member of several professional societies, the author of numerous papers, active in community service committees in Seattle, and the moderator of a television program called "All About Life". He is now a member of the faculty of the Department of Obstetrics and Gynecology and the Director of the Division of Family Planning and Sex Education at the University of Washington.

Dr. Pion will speak on "Pregnancy Detection and Community Outreach".

Pregnancy Detection and Community Outreach

RONALD J. PION, M.D.
Director, Division of Family Planning and Sex Education,
University of Washington School of Medicine, Seattle

When Dr. Kaufman was at the University of Washington in Seattle, I don't believe that we had a Division of Family Planning and Sex Education in the Medical School. That's a story we could perhaps spend more time discussing during the panel period.

In listening to Dr. Combs describe the potential areas of research involvement of our government in supporting and encouraging research in the complexities of the area, I enjoyed hearing in the last few minutes of his address the concept of mission-oriented research - missionary oriented research - research involving missionaries whose orientation is problem solving.

I would like to discuss with you today mission-oriented research. The moral and ethical perspective from which I, as an individual, operate, would perhaps be a good place to begin. I have been misquoted out of context so often in the past, and will continue to be misquoted so often in the future, that at least I can begin, not defensively, but hopefully, by describing a moral, ethical perspective. I don't think pregnancies should occur by accident. I find it paradoxical still in 1970 that we plan conferences, as we plan research centers, as we plan heart transplantations, as we plan moon shots, we continue to have babies conceived as haphazard accidents of sexual behavior. This is immoral to me.

Another moral and ethical perspective I should like to begin with is that to which I alluded yesterday. As we continue to export our expertise to underdeveloped nations in the area of family planning, we are singularly lacking in credibility and validity in our own country. There is no model-family planning community anywhere in the United States. It would be nice as we export our expertise to do so with validity.

I am a family planning activist. As a family planning activist interested in population planning, I would remind all of you this morning - because it is easy to become confused in the course of a two day, or a five day conference - that family planning and population planning are separate and distinct. For purposes again of exploring with you somewhat later in depth, let's consider (a) sexual awareness, (b) family planning, (c) birth planning (I think births should occur within families), and (d) population planning. That's four separate items - sexual awareness, family planning, birth planning, population planning - all of which are necessary components to bring about what many of us think is necessary, namely population stabilization, so that we all have an opportunity to solve those problems that exist now.

With 200 million people in this country plus - not plus or minus - a potentially anticipated additional 100 million in some thirty to thirty-five years, if we increase by one-half the number of people we now have, with as many problems unsolved as we now have, I cannot believe that the problems in the year 2000 are going to be easier to resolve.

The title of my paper this morning is "Pregnancy Detection and Community Outreach". It's a response to the young lady's frustration yesterday afternoon - "what can people do". On March 1st of this year, we hope, all things going well, to open a model Family Planning Clinic at the University of Washington. We have had family planning at the University of Washington since the mid 50's; we have had an active, heavily involved Planned Parenthood of Seattle for 37 years; we have family planning clinics in our Public Health Departments; we have family planning clinics in our County Hospital; we have family planning ongoing in the offices of private physicians in Seattle; we have a Washington State Council of Family Planning that was formed in the latter part of 1969; we hope to have a Washington State Council in Population Planning at the end of 1970.

With all of this, why do we need a model Family Planning Clinic at the University, when I just told you we have family planning at the University? Well, for one thing, in dealing with mission-oriented research, we would like to define for people what family planning really is, and stop, as I suggested yesterday, using it euphemistically for birth control. Let's talk about family planning as a comprehensive health service - social service, theologic service, community service. Certainly not limited to the province of medicine. Some of my own problems are that my good colleagues - in my respected profession - (I do have a lot of respect for medicine still) - have considered family planning as birth control, and continue to do so.

What will our model Family Planning Clinic comprise? It will be a sterilization consultation center; it will respond to people in the community who have completed their family size and who wish to use a permanent method of contraception. People of the United States - and my remarks are all confined to the people of the United States because that's where I live - the people of the United States do not understand that sterilization is a permanent method of contraception. It should be used by people who have completed their family size.

A body to which I belong, called the American College of Obstetricians and Gynecologists, saw fit, in 1965, to revise the section of the manual of standards dealing with sterilization, and they, in all their anticipatory professionalism, allowed sterilization (e.g. tubal ligation) to be considered - if a woman was 35 and had three children, was 30 and had four children, or was 25 and had five children - a significant milestone in this history of the College because the numbers of children you had to have before 1965 were significantly greater before you could be considered for sterilization. In 1969 another revision was made in the manual of standards. Now, the numbers game suddenly disappeared from the manual. Now, we talk about individualization in the area of sterilization. You can rest assured that the translation of concern to action (the title of a Presidential Commission dealing with family planning) in this area of sterilization amongst obstetricians and gynecologists first, and amongst general practitioners secondly, with a little luck might be less than ten years.

A good colleague of mine in the Northwest insists that a woman have at least eight children before she be considered for sterilization. He was trained by other medical educators, and I, as a medical educator, share in the responsibility for any kind of strange behavior on the part of physicians. If physicians behave strangely, it is because they have been taught to behave strangely by preceding generations of strangely behaving physicians.

The second area of the model Family Planning Clinic would encompass a rape consultation center. Sexual assault can and does occur in communities to women in the reproductive age group (it is one thing to try and stamp out rape and it is difficult because that is a complex problem); but within any community, if pregnancy occurs as a consequence of rape, the community is guilty and I indict the community. Any case of rape must be allowed to come somewhere for attention, treatment and counseling, and prevention of pregnancy - a consequence of rape. The technology has been available for years - the application is lacking in most communities of the United States - in all communities of the United States, in terms of an advertised service so that law enforcement officers could refer victims to a relevant service. At such a center doctors could do something other than take sperm slides so that evidence is available for the courts. What are we concerned about? Evidence that sperm exists in a vagina, or preventing a pregnancy from occurring?

The Family Planning Clinic will provide marital and non-marital counseling in the area of family planning. People who have problems; people who are confused; people who want to understand, could come to the center. Perhaps we could help them. Counseling in the area of sexual conflict should be made available for the unmarried as well as for those married. Would you believe that non-marital counseling must be made available in the sexual conflict area? The need exists.

Genetic counseling will be provided - done in the life style not only of the poor, but also of the rich - so that aspects of disease may be considered before a couple considers a pregnancy. I share with Dr. Gyorgy this morning a fantasy I have always had of two women meeting in a market. One says to the other: "Gee, it's been five years since I have seen you; you have been married; how many children do you have?" And she said "none". "No children in five years, why?" "My hemoglobin is only 9".

Why not give a child an advantageous start? Why not have a hemoglo - bin of 12 or 13 before a couple conceives a child? Because it has not been our style.

Infertility counseling will be a part of the model family planning clinic, so that people who want to be pregnant don't have to stay married for five years and wonder what is wrong with their husbands, or what's wrong with themselves, before they go and find out about having a baby. Adoption will be offered as a viable alternative from the beginning; not after two years of blowing out one's tubes and taking x-rays, and saying: "I really don't know what's wrong with you as a couple, but have you ever considered adopting a child"?

Premarital counseling will be widely available at the model Family Planning Clinic, and people might be advised not to marry. Advised not to marry yet because financially, and psychologically, and emotionally, they seem ill prepared. Advised - not forced either to marry or not to marry. I think it's time we stopped forcing people to marry.

We will offer abortion counseling at the model Family Planning Clinic. More on that controversial topic in a moment.

What I am trying to say in this very brief and hopefully provocative address is something about the family planning process which involves identifying the sexually active person in the community who doesn't want to become pregnant as a result of sexual activity, and providing her (and him) with the means of avoiding the possibility of unplanned, unwanted conception, which, by the way, differs from unplanned, unwanted pregnancy, which differs from unwanted or wanted children at birth. You can plan a conception, you can want a pregnancy, you can want a child, and even then you can grow angrier than the devil when that child is fifteen and is rebellious and drops acid and smokes pot, and you are not sure that you did the right thing in having him in the first place.

Wantedness is a dynamic concept! You can want your first child to bury you in this culture or other cultures, and you can want that it be a male child; and you can have five daughters and try for that first male child and have a sixth daughter. Perhaps the law that we would like to see changed culturally is that families must have at least one child - so that that child can carry on the business of the family. Natural or adopted - male or female. We were talking about No. 1, No. 2 and No. 3 sons on the way over here this morning. Why can't we have No. 1 child,

No. 2 child, No. 3 child - in those cultures that might next year still consider the morality of three children ? I have three children - but neither my wife nor I had been educated to the fact that two children - in terms of the world situation - was a moral responsibility for all couples to consider.

I end with a word on abortion, although I obviously don't want to end. My bag is verbalizing my problems. Very soon I hope all of us will stop talking about abortion. Someone told me this morning that one of the religious groups in this State, if it's correct and we can establish its correctness, is going to have some kind of anti-abortion Sunday tomorrow.

I don't like abortions because I am a product of this culture. It is a "potentially dehumanizing process". Putting an ileostomy in someone's stomach is potentially a dehumanizing process in our culture; putting a colostomy in someone's abdomen is a potentially dehumanizing process in our culture; taking off a person's breasts for a bilateral malignancy is a Potentially dehumanizing process; taking off half a jaw for malignancy of the mandible is a potentially dehumanizing process in our culture. So what? What has that got to do with taking care of people? I don't mean to compare any of the operative procedures I just mentioned with abortion. That was not the purpose of mentioning other potentially dehumanizing procedures.

I am talking about problem solving. Now the hangup as I see it - in my opinion - in our culture and other cultures - is that we don't deal with inducing menstrual periods. And this is not a game that I am suggesting to you. If we advertised a center, and that center can be in a physician's office anywhere, and hopefully some day in an office that may be supervised by a physician, but other responsive people are there too, who are qualified to care for the patient. I don't know why only physicians have to be the ones involved in the family planning process. We might talk about that during the panel discussion. I want to know what women out there in a community are late in their menstrual function, because I want them to know that they are at risk of being pregnant.

I want the problem solving process for the couple to occur when the couple is late. Because the couple is then at risk of being pregnant. Does the couple want to be pregnant? I will not advise them to come back in three weeks when the pregnancy test is likely to be positive because I can't tell now. I will ask the couple to come in and consider the risk of pregnancy, for them, for the potential child, for the family, for society. The question I will put to the couple would be - do you want to continue the risk of potentially being pregnant, or would you like to have your menstrual period induced? We would like to have our menstrual period induced - thank you doctor. We could then use physical, chemical, and mechanical means of inducing a menstrual period. We hope to sponsor a conference later this year directed to the subject of "Inducing Menstrual Periods for Women in Their Reproductive Years". We would hope at that conference to discuss the use of laser beams and other Orwellian methods for inducing menstrual flow. We must begin to deal with problem solving. And let's stop talking about when life begins in this particular process because we don't have mass Sunday demonstrations about "thou shalt not kill", except in time of war. I know that certain people who are snuffed out like that - I know without question - that there is a quality of life there; not only a potential for human life that is being snuffed out, but a human life that is being snuffed out.

Let me hear the hiearchy of all major religious groups talk about the immorality of war and an immediate cessation to all wars forever from now on. If they will do that, I will talk to them about when life begins - potentially. It's an abstract theology; there is not a scientist in the world who knows when life beings; there is not a theologian who knows when life begins. Let's take care of people and let's take care of our environmental and societal problems and let's begin to do it yesterday.

Thank you.

Panel Discussion

Dr. William Kaufman - Chairman

Dr. Ronald J. Pion

Dr. Jerry W. Combs, Jr.

Dr. Jeremy Green

Dr. Ruth E. Hartley

Miss Sharon A. Estel,
Sophomore Student, UWGB

DR. KAUFMAN:

In our society abortion is a dirty word. It is illegal and most people consider it immoral. It is a serious problem - a problem for profound thought. Figures are difficult to obtain, but it is stated that, despite the illegality, between one and 2 million women a year in the United States seek and obtain abortions, and about 4,000 proved fatal. Almost one million of these abortions are performed on women who are married and have two or three children.

Let me begin our panel discussion by introducing the members. The ladies first - on my left, Dr. Ruth Hartley, Chairman of the Concentration in Growth and Development here in the College of Human Biology; Dr. Hartley did her doctorate at Columbia; she is a clinical psychologist, diplomate of the American Board of Professional Psychology and the author of many papers, and several books. She was at the University of Hawaii before joining our staff.

On my right, Miss Sharon A. Estel, a student in the College of Human Biology. A local girl, she graduated from Luxemburg-Casco High School, and plans to teach in secondary schools.

On the far right, again Dr. Ronald J. Pion, Director of the Division of Family Planning and Sex Education at the University of Washington.

Just to my right, Dr. Jeremy Green, who did his medical education in Johannesburg, South Africa, and studied in Ireland and England before coming to Green Bay. He has been in private practice in internal medicine in Green Bay since 1964. On my left again, Dr. Jerry Combs of the Center for Population Research, Chief of Behavioral Sciences.

On the far left, our speaker from last evening, Mr. Robert McLaughlin, a member of the Office of Population in the International Division of the Ford Foundation.

DR. HERBERT SANDMIRE:

I would like to address my remarks to Dr. Pion. First of all, in general, to support what he said about reluctance to tubal ligations; but to point out that there are other reasons other than strange behavior for this reluctance. You have to go back to 1935 when the first legislative statute relating to sterilization was passed, and there were subsequent ones that were done primarily to permit mental defectives to be sterilized - an eugenic provision. There has been no subsequent law in this field, but because this statute permitted sterilization in mentally defectives, it was erroneously assumed that it prohibited this procedure in people who weren't mentally defective. The medical profession had an area of confusion. Generally, the medical profession tries to follow what they think the public wants, in addition to what they think the patient wants. The medical profession is not always able to interpret properly, or correctly, what the public wants; and if there is an area here of deficiency it's of misinterpretation, rather than of strange behavior on the part of the doctors.

Furthermore, to emphasize that other people misinterpret what the public wants, the politicians also misinterpret. The State Medical Society attempted to get an Attorney General opinion to clarify this issue for three years in succession, and the Attorney General, anticipating running for Governor, politically made what he considered to be the correct response. He didn't respond to this request. So, if the doctors have misinterpreted, so have the politicians; and it's the job of symposia like this to enlighten the physicians into what the public is after.

Furthermore, we were told yesterday that one of the factors involved in successful population stabilization in Japan was that the doctors came home from the war, they had nothing to do, they were greedy, so they liberalized the abortion law, and presto - we have a country with 90 million people who are able to stabilize their population. I would be much more interested in what motivated the people in Japan to go to their physicians who returned from the war and liberalized the abortion law. I think the primary decision was with the people. They did decide that they had to stabilize the population. I think a lot more could be learned by finding out what made them think they should stabilize the population, rather than giving too much credit to the doctors who didn't have enough to do. So, in terms of tubal ligations, Dr. Pion and I talked about this, and it's true we haven't used this method of birth control to the extent that we will be using it in the very near future. Thank you.

DR. KAUFMAN:

Dr. Sandmire is a specialist in obstetrics and gynecology here in Green Bay. Dr. Pion, do you want to comment?

DR. PION:

I guess I sometimes see my job, Dr. Sandmire, as a provacateur (gadfly). I like filling the role because I think people often need to be provoked into relevant and responsive action. Doctors don't talk enough to lawyers, lawyers don't talk enough to doctors, and a lot of us don't necessarily understand and look for reasons why there has been a degree of inactivity in a certain area. For example, just to provoke again, if doctors really thought more of public opinion, then maybe the A.M.A. wouldn't have objected to group practice, and maybe the A.M.A. wouldn't have objected to the voluntary health insurance schemes (30 and more years ago.) Maybe we would have socialized medicine in this country tomorrow if it was public opinion that doctors were always interested in following. If we do a heart transplantation, we then go out and teach lawyers and community people how to recognize when death has occurred. Medical leadership, legal leadership, political leadership, academic leadership - we are talking about recognizing problems, confronting

116

problems and putting forth alternative solutions. We don't have to like the alternatives. We must, however, recognize what they are, and then we have to have a town meeting and begin to decide on which of the alternatives this community - mine, yours, somebody else's - will begin to opt for so that we just don't let things continue to happen.

If we have an empty lot across the street, and beer cans and litter bags begin to appear on that empty lot, a demographer, potentially interested in beer cans, can begin to record the number of beer cans appearing in 1953, follow it up annually, and in 1959 make a projection for 1965; and based upon the annual increment, state that in 1969 we are going to have X number of beer cans. He, or she, could have underestimated, or overestimated, but in 1969 we can do an evaluation and find out whether the projection was carefully arrived at. But in 1953, you could have gone across the street and picked up the beer cans. I don't think for a minute that Dr. Taeuber believes that the reason Japan has an abortion policy that was liberalized was because of the greed of physicians.

SARAH WATKE (Green Bay Press Gazette):

Dr. Pion, yesterday in the panel you mentioned that you thought religions had some obligation to help people understand, I believe it was, differences in procreativity and sexual relations. And, I was wondering today after your talk, would you comment in general - first, on the role of the religions in the attitudes, maybe keeping it to this country; and then - secondly, elaborate more on what you meant about religions having an obligation in this area.

DR. PION:

I prefer to use the general term "religions" because I feel too many people like to put the whole obstructionist thing on the Catholics, and this is unfair. There are sincere fundamentalists; there are sincere Mormons; and sincere people in almost any religious group you can find who are concerned about all of the issues we have been discussing - concerned and "obstructionistic". Probably, for valid reasons of sincerity. I think it's too easy to say "Boy, we would have different things if it weren't for those Catholics"!

In the area of sex education, I think the primary responsibility, for example, lies with parents - if for no other reason than parents have kids for the first six years of life, when the real things happen, and the real formative direction is set, by whether daddy beats mommy, or screams at mommy, or disrespects, abuses mommy, and vice versa - long before the kid ever gets to school. If the kid is lucky enough to be brought up in a religious home - and I remind you that all children in America are not - if a child is lucky enough to be brought up in a religious home, then I think the religion has an obligation to expand upon and direct the family and the child to future responsibility.

Parents cop out; religion cops out, especially in the area of sex. And I think it's because adults generally have dirty minds. I think adults have dirty minds because they haven't been helped. They have not had an education in an area of honest to goodness what it's like to be a boy growing into being a man; and what it is to be a girl growing up to be a woman. But you say sex education and someone says - "uh, uh, now they're going to teach intercourse in the schools". Now, why do they think that they are going to teach intercourse in the schools when someone raises the word sex education? And why do people become labeled Communists, or dupes of the Communist conspiracy - except that adults are very dirty minded people, I believe, because they haven't been helped. All of us must learn. If we must begin with adult education, by all means, let's begin with adult education, and let's have that adult education begin in the church - because it's a good, upstanding institution. It's hard to knock the church. Fine. Let the church then get involved in solutions to the population problem. Let Jerry Combs answer with a contractual agreement with the major religious institutions of the United States for them to come up with theologic solutions to the environmental problems, to population problems, to abortion, to all things. I feel quite strongly that the major religious groups must help their followers understand the real distinction that exists between a sexual ethic and a reproductive ethic. The latter should be oriented to the, as yet, unconceived child - what are its needs? A sexual ethic must concern itself in a much more comprehensive way with relationships between people - rather than with the process of coitus.

DR. KAUFMAN:

Dr. Hartley, as a psychologist and with your interest in the roles of the sexes in society, would you comment on this.

DR. HARTLEY:

I think Dr. Pion has done it very, very ably. I was thinking as he was talking that I don't have to carry the torch this time.

DR. PION:

Then I can be called the bad guy of the conference.

DR. HARTLEY:

That was not my intention.

DR. PION:

I know.

DR. HARTLEY:

I will gladly share the burden with you.

PAUL HAYES (Milwaukee Journal):

This is for Dr. Pion, and it's a question from a newspaper that has practical problems. In Milwaukee not very long ago, there was such a public outcry, largely along religious lines, against a proposal to even seek Federal funds for free birth control, family planning clinics to serve Milwaukee's poor, that the proposal for a time failed. Which leads to these questions about your clinic - your model Family Planning Clinic - what political problems, if any, have you had? How widespread is the publicity of your clinic, and well, in general, have you met with this kind of a reaction?

DR. PION:

We asked our University educational television station in 1966 if they would allow us to do a television program on sex and society. We went through lots of planning pains. We did a program for twenty-six weeks - one hour each week. We were given sign-off time. Station programming went off at 10. We were allowed on at 10. We paid, as another University department, for overtime to appear on educational television at our University. We decided that if there was an angry response on the part of the community, we would invite those who were angry to appear on television. We did this for twenty-eight weeks and I think the fact that it was one of the most successful educational television programs in the community, as judged by the numbers of responsive letters and calls - both angry and supportive - was an indication that we were serving a function.

A colleague, Dr. Wagner, head of our clinical psychology training program, who works with us in our Division, followed with 13 (one hour) programs geared to parents of teenagers about sex. It was a telecourse offered through University Extension; guidelines were available for those wishing to take the telecourse. The success of the programs related to the participants.

One anecdotal tale concerns the participation of a nun - a woman I admire greatly - who does not wear her habit very often; she teaches developmental psychology and is on the staff at Seattle University. She appeared on the program one night and we were talking about the development of the child. Although I didn't ask her to put on her habit, she wore it. And she spoke about penis envy and masturbation along with other items that are important in childhood development. And to have a Sister in a habit talk about penis envy and masturbation, believe you me, is one heck of a breakthrough. She is marvelous because she's comfortable and because she is an expert.

We had many religions represented. We had many phases of the community represented, including people from our "ghetto area", talking about the problems and myths of sexuality. During all of this time, my president, Dr. Charles Odegaard, received letters from people who thought they were politically strong, as well as from people who weren't politically strong, wanting to do something about me and the program. We invited them on the program; some came. They were heard in open forum. We then did a program called "All About Life", which Dr. Kaufman alluded to before, where I appeared with three children. I am a ham. I do like talking. I dressed up the children (one black, one white, and one female - I believe sexism exists as does racism) in high intern collars. They were all eight years of age and we asked them to serve as our consultants. The direction of the program was towards an exploration of family and values and how pregnancy occurs within families, and how many children families consider having. We talked about pregnancy: we introduced "dirty" words such as penis, vagina, ovaries, testicles, spermatogenesis, oogenesis, and all the obscenities that the media, including newspapers, void. They have headlines concerning massacres and killing and maiming, and all the words that I find obscene in the media, which no one questions.

What are newspapers doing about the problems in any community? I know a series is done, and I know an article will appear about this Symposium in Green Bay; and like the Shriner's Parade, once the last strains of music disappear down the street, we forget all about the parade until the next time it comes around. You have a weather forecast box in your newspaper. It's often inaccurate. Why couldn't you have a population forecast box in your newspaper, reporting daily the population for the world, the United States, Brown County, and Green Bay, every day, perhaps inaccurately, available to you from the Population Reference Bureau, or any other number of sources, because population as a forecast is much more important than the weather. We have gotten into lots of trouble - potential and real - most of it has been unreal. As I suggested to the new's lady earlier, because I like quoting classical literature, Pogo has said: "we have encountered the enemy and they is us".

DR. KAUFMAN:

I feel I should make a small claim here. It was on that same television station which Dr. Pion talks about that I participated in one of the very early sex education programs at the University of Washington in Seattle - about 15 years ago, when a panel at 10 o'clock in the evening, discussed The Golden Ass of Apuleius, and anyone of you who has ever read it, know that it is sex education.

DR. ABRAHAMSON:

Have you ever received a grant or contract proposal, Dr. Combs, from any of the institutions that Dr. Pion mentioned a few minutes ago?

DR. COMBS:

As a matter of fact, as Dr. Pion and I have already discussed privately, we have been wanting to develop research in this area, but very few proposals have been submitted.

DR. ABRAHAMSON:

From the churches, etc.

DR. COMBS:

No, not from the churches.

DR. ABRAHAMSON:

I don't mean from a school - from a church?

DR. COMBS:

No, not yet. This is one of the very critical fields that we would like to encourage. I don't know quite how to make the specifications for this research. It seems to me that in the field of religion, what is involved are think pieces which make a critical examination of the moral principles and look at the consequences of these, and look them over to see if they are not out of step with the times. The truth of the matter is that this process has gone on for generations, for centuries, this process of evaluating positions taken and adapting the principles to fit the new conditions.

In this whole field of population research and population action, it seems to me that we are right now in the process of looking at old tenets, evaluating them in terms of their personal consequences, community consequences, social consequences, and coming up with some new frames of reference in which we can maintain the old values, while establishing new guidelines for behavior. To expand on this just a little bit, our institutional arrangements only slowly adapt to changed conditions. Because of the tedious way in which people, acting individually in solving their problems, put their institutional arrangements together and learn to work cooperatively, collectively and in concert, we always approach new problems with institutional arrangements that were designed to solve yesterday's problems. Thus, one of the difficulties, whenever you start to solve new problems, is not only to make adjustments to solve this particular problem, but to bring the whole society into concert so that the institutions reinforce one another. One of the points we might mention, we have gone through a process of rethinking our sexual attitudes in this society. It has been going on for a long time. We rebelled against the rigidity, and personal consequences of too rigid regulation of sex as reflected in some of our moral attitudes. On the other hand, the society's institutional arrangements, and what we were willing to do about them, didn't keep pace. The result is that we have a recent generation that is much freerer in its sexual activity, but we have an increase in illegitimacy, teenage pregnancy, increase in early marriage, increased demand for abortions, for such agencies as the Salvation Army and the Florence Chrittenden Home - because we didn't at the same time make other provisions that were compatible with a more relaxed attitude of sexual behavior.

DR. KAUFMAN:

I would like to address a question to Mr. McLaughlin and to Dr. Combs. They may decline to answer if they wish. Both are members of organizations which do some research, but are largely responsible for granting money for research. Do you feel that the funds are adequate to do the job - are more than adequate, or that they present any real problem in getting the job of research in this area done?

DR. COMBS:

Last year the funds made available to, and the proposals approved for funding by the Center, exactly matched. Actually, we could have made more money available if we had had more good proposals, but if we had had them, some good research in contraceptive development would have had to be postponed. There is a shortage of competent personnal in the Behavioral Sciences who are at the same time ready and willing and eager to attack these particular problems. At the same time, we have perhaps not entirely mined the potential area for research. As more able investigators are attracted to the program, the demands for funds will undoubtedly increase.

We think, therefore, that it is going to be nip and tuck within the next couple of years, as more and more people become aware of the program, and as we are able to talk more specifically with people about the kind of proposals that are well within our area of research, even with a projected increase in funds. As you can recognize from the outline of the program we have, we could increase the present 2.3 million dollars being spent in Behavioral Science research by ten times to get 23 million, by 10 to get 230 million, and so on; and it still wouldn't amount to the money we have spent on a great many other social problems. But there will necessarily continue to be the problem of maintaining funding in some relationship with the number of competent people able to produce good research in this field.

MR. McLAUGHLIN:

I represent an organization which has been urging for many years that the Federal Government of the United States, and indeed many governments around the world, should allocate far higher sums of money for research, not only on the social science side of the population question, but also on the technical or reproductive biology side of that question. I recognize the problem that Dr. Combs mentioned of the relative lack of trained personnel, and, therefore, the possible lack of high quality research proposals. However, I think we would still be in the position of urging a far greater expenditure of Federal money, first to support the training institutions that will produce the scientists that will submit the high quality proposals, and second, to finance the proposals themselves. When we think of numbers, a number that was suggested a few years ago was an annual level of research expenditure of 150 million dollars. We still stand by that figure.

IRIS FONTERA:

All of you are involved in different aspects of this field, so this question is directed to any of you. Do you really believe that we can wait around, that we have the time to wait around for the institutions to come around, and the people to come around, or are we going to see the time when the government is going to have to say, for example, "two children or in jail". Do you think people will do it without the laws?

DR. KAUFMAN:

Let me ask Miss Estel. There are changing attitudes throughout the world, here in the United States, and perhaps here in Green Bay as well. Miss Estel represents the younger people and she may have some feelings as to whether population control will have to be enforced or if people will do it voluntarily?

SHARON ESTEL:

I have thought of this before and I am still thinking on it. I don't know. I think sooner or later the government will have to take a stand and tell us you have to do this, or you can't do that, you cannot have more than this number of children. I don't know because I guess we are people and people don't always do exactly what other people think they should.

DR. GREEN:

When I was asked to come on this panel, I really hand't thought too much about the population explosion, but then I began to read a great deal. And I began to listen to television, and I am sure some of you, perhaps two or three nights ago on the Johnny Carson Show, may have heard Dr. Paul Ehrlich. Certainly, if you didn't hear him, and I think this has already been recommended, buy his book and read it.

There are several things that have impressed me about things that I have read. There are certain irrefutable facts, - and I don't want to talk in terms of philosophical discussions until time immemorial- but there are irrefutable facts about population growth, about subnutrition with the present world's population, and what will happen in the year 2000. I think a great limiting factor is time, and we don't have time. When I look around at the people in Green Bay, and when I look at my colleagues, the physicians in Green Bay, and I hear so many people say we should start with the ghetto areas, that we should start dispensing contraceptive literature and contraceptive devices to the ghetto areas - I look at the physicians in Green Bay and see physicians with ten or more children. I think that we have to attack affluent society and the great apathy that exists in society today. I just have to say this as a dig at the medical profession because I happen to be pretty vocal about a number of things the medical profession does, but when I look around this audience today and see only two other physicians from Green Bay, this to me is apathy.

If we wait for people to start doing these things, it is inconceivable to me that we will ever solve this problem. I think that there are going to have to be government enforced controls. You are going to have to be told that to have more than two children is a crime against society. You can no longer make the excuse that you will have as many children as you wish because you think that you can afford to educate them as you wish. I really believe this, because we don't have time.

DR. KAUFMAN:

Dr. Pion called for leadership in the medical profession, in academic circles, and throughout the United States, to which I reply "hear, hear". I would ask Dr. Hartley about the psychology of the response of a public in a voluntary program and a government enforced program of population control?

DR. HARTLEY:

I think any coercion inevitably produces a reaction - a negative reaction - so that I question whether government coercion would be accepted amicably. I am not sure how it would work out. It might work, but I don't think it would last very long if we maintain our current system of government. On the voluntary side, obviously massive education campaigns have to be mounted. However, I agree with Dr. Pion, there isn't much point to the massive education campaigns unless you make the means of implementing those campaigns available to all the people and make them available without any of the negative sanctions that are now attached, in the opinion of many people, to visibly taking advantage of their availability. It's not really a simple question we have opened here, but it is a question that must have answers. I think we are irresponsible, and, if you will, immoral, if we shirk the job that's implied here. Was that definite enough for you?

DR. KAUFMAN:

Thank you. There is one irrefutable fact. It takes time to establish programs, to get a consensus, to make regulations, to make laws, but everyone of us present and everyone who may hear this as an individual, can begin a program of population control and family planning immediately.

DR. COMBS:

Let me make just a couple of footnotes to this. Without laws, the United States and various countries in Western Europe at various times, have brought their population growth down to the replacement level. It seems to me that it is likely to take as long to establish a base of public opinion to support certain types of legislation as it would to bring a large segment of the population into conformity with certain standards without laws. The questions ultimately boil down to whether this is a better way than using economic incentives or certain negative incentives, or certain tax regulations, etc., or altering your institutional structure in certain ways so that more birth control is practiced. It's a choice of means. Anyway you take it, reduction in fertility is largely a question of public desire. I agree with Dr. Hartley. If you pass a law which nobody would obey, or a very large percentage of the people would flaunt, you would have problems of enforcement that might make it as ridiculous as prohibition, or some of the other things we try to regulate without success.

DR. PION:

I wish to expand on some of Mr. McLaughlin's remarks of last night. We have had a proposal kicking around for some time and we have no idea if that particular proposal will be funded. I am all for talking about governmental coercion because I think we should talk about it. And the optimism that I share with Dr. Gyorgy is such that I think that while we talk about things like that, for heaven's sakes, let's do what is proper, what is humane, and bring it about without law - because I really think we can. The reason I think we can is because I am very familiar with what is not being done. The kinds of things that are not being done has to do with something again alluded to yesterday by someone.

What is the power influencing body of American today and I think to a large degree it's the "boob tube"? At future symposiums when we talk about mass communication and family planning, whether he's right or wrong, let's have McLuhan here. See, I want the Ford Foundation, Rockefeller Foundation, the Population Council, and the Office of Population Research, and every other group to begin looking at "Sesame Street". Now, I don't know how many of you have seen Sesame Street because educational TV is apparently not all that available locally. But somebody should be insisting that it comes over CBS, NBC or ABC. It's a preschool program that doesn't teach "Ultra-Bright" jingles, but it does use the commercial medium to teach A, B, C and D, and numerals and words and concepts that kids walk away from the "boob tube" whistling and humming and learning. The revolution that we should see should be in education and there are many things we haven't done yet in education - like not starting a new college campus, but bringing all of the talent that could start a new campus into the preschool and the elementary school. Why don't we pay - here's a little reverse sexism - why don't we pay, Ph.D. males, to teach in kindergarten? Dr. Storey said a little something about leisure time and all of us are pretty much aware of what isn't going on with fathering. Without the big argument in terms of permissiveness leading us all astray, I wonder about male imagery, male modelling in our society. You know, a lot of kids learn about male modelling from Chuck Conners (Rifleman); a lot of kids learn about male modelling from "Eddie's Father"; a lot of kids learn about male modelling from the "boob tube". The "boob tube" is an extremely powerful tool that has not yet been utilized.

Again, sure, Paul Ehrlich comes on the Johnny Carson Show. Great. Good. More often. Let him talk about coercive measures that the government should use and let somebody sit back and say "Oh, My God, no". Let's do something else too.

You know, a brilliant woman in Hawaii said to a Chamber of Commerce group of males one day: "Which would you rather have, abortion repeal or compulsory pregnancy"? And they sat around for a couple of minutes and said: "My God, we can't have compulsory pregnancy". What are the alternatives when explored in depth? If we get, in addition to Sesame Street, Marcus Welby, and General Hospital, and Medical Center, dealing with content, because the people watch it for entertainment, and not a panel group - because people switch off panel groups - the bulk of the people - let's begin to utilize that which is so very obvious to us. What about commercials? What about tonight when we all watch the "boob tube" - and lots of us don't admit how often we watch it - what if for 60 seconds the following appears: an open field (I would like to find out who finds this offensive, by the way) - an open field appears, and every second, three newborn infants are superimposed on the open field. There is a stop watch in the upper right hand corner of the TV screen, tic - tic - tic - tic - tic. And then a rising cacophony of newborn sounds begin to stimulate the auditory apparatus as well. During the 60 seconds, 180 newborn infants make their appearance. And a voice at the end says: "Did you know that during the last 60 seconds of this announcement 180 newborn infants were added to the world's population? Is the world ready for them? Brought to you by Creative Family Planning".

MR. McLAUGHLIN:

I think I will return the favor and just add one footnote or interpretation to what Ron has said. I think that there is inevitably going to be in this country and in many countries a political dynamic, or dialog, among various types of proposals, and that as the perception of population growth increases, as more and more people are aware, as some of the more coercive schemes are suggested, and publicized, then I think the reaction will be among many people who have up to now been apathetic: "But certainly we are not going to go that far - isn't there some intermediate step that doesn't violate our values"? As Ron has suggested, and many people have suggested, in this country and all over the world, yes, there are many steps possible that do not violate our basic values.

DR. KAUFMAN:

You asked how long would it take. Until we reduce the present rate of population growth, the world's population will continue to increase at something like 70 million every year, so add that up for the five years, or ten years.

DR. PION:

We are making the commercials. Whether we can get them on prime network time, and how to go about doing this, is a question we should talk about.

DR. KAUFMAN:

Dr. Pion will take orders for shares of stock right after this.

DR. PION:

It's a non-profit corporation.

DR. PIERRE SLIGHTAM:

I insist that as there are only three physicians in this room from
Green Bay that I know of, I insist that I be heard from. My name is
Pierre Slightam and I am a family practitioner here in Green Bay. And
I have seven children. And I agree with Dr. Pion. I think he's a real
bright light here. The whole bag here is in education and as a family
practitioner, I feel that this is my primary job - to try to teach
people how to live. Now, I am not expounding - I am not saying that
everybody should have seven children. I came yesterday morning with
the idea that maybe I would learn a little bit more, clarify a bit more,
develop a little more hindsight and help people, as it is becoming more
mandatory to help people avoid little family dilemnas like I have created at 1005 So. Clay St. I have not only seven lovely children, I have
seven lovely girls. So I am familiar with his term "sexism".

Yesterday some comments were made, and then I got into a discussion
at noon, which revolves around some of my primary interests. We have
at home now a lovely four month old child, and she is the picture of
health, and beauty, and our pride and joy right now, and our girls are
all proud of her, and I am very proud of her. My wife is one of the rare
women in our apparently artificial contraceptive society, as we are referred to, who breast feeds. And I didn't come with this in mind yesterday morning, but as we are dealing with malnutrition, nutrition, ecology,
population problems, birth control and all, I was a little bit stimulated
by some of the remarks yesterday morning, but, in particular, one which
Dr. Gyorgy made about the need in this country to return to a much more
reasonable, humane, form of feeding our infants - breast feeding. It's
quite simple, you know. We are the only animal in the animal kingdom
that rejects our young at birth and feeds them something else. I cate-
gorize this up in the back of my head - what you have said - and I was
disappointed that you didn't illuminate on this a little further. You
mentioned the LaLeche League, and it just happens that my wife is a
little active in this in the Green Bay community; and the LaLeche League
here is having problems getting the support of the physicians in the
community, getting the support of the hospitals, and the nurseries. I
can tell you from my own personal experience, I really feel that in family
planning, contraception, birth control, healthy mothering and nutrition,
this is very important.

Yesterday we went from this Symposium to a meeting with one of the
doctors who was here from Madison, Dr. Mark Hanson, and we were talking
about the physician dilemna in Wisconsin - the need to resume an education

of the type of physician who is going to be concerned about these things: namely, a family physician. We have shortages in this area. And, to exemplify - to make an example of how I thought a certain type of family physician would be able to pull off a revival in this type of thing, and this type of education, that I think is very important along with the tube, and along with universities and colleges and sex education in the schools - I, working with families, have to work directly with the family unit. Throughout the example in our discussion on how we are going to get a certain type of family doctor, is Dr. Gyorgy's statement that we ought to bring breast feeding back into this country. I feel that a type of physician who deals with kids, who deals with mothers, who deals with the total family structure, would really be able to help in this area. It was fantastic! I started immediately an argument about the breast in our physician group, and finally one physician said: "let's keep the breast out of this discussion". I didn't mean this at all. All I was talking about was family practice. I really would like to ask some of the panel who are interested in physiology, reproduction, and all, how this type of infant nutrition and feeding would affect the population explosion in our country, if we really did it. Has anybody got any ideas on this?

DR. PION:

You are saying a whole lot at once. And it's hard to respond on all levels. One of the things that I hear and respond to quickly is the fact that "yeah, yeah, sure, by all means", Let's take, you know, the breasts of women, reaffirm what they are for, change the whole myth of sexual exploitation away from Heffnerian responses, away from all sorts of things and attributes we have given the human breast, and let's tell women, long before they plan their first child, about the gratification many women have when they breast feed; about the very wonderful studies that have been done by Dr. Gyorgy amongst others, the Drs. Newton, and so many people, about the advantages of breast feeding. Aside from its economic advantage and efficiency, let's tell women that not to breast feed might deprive them of a sexual pleasure. That's real honest to goodness talk. Talk to women who breast feed and enjoy breast feeding. And when you offer an incentive of sexual pleasure, you know you really might get people to breast feed.

DR. KAUFMAN:

May we move this on please? Rather than a discussion of the medical problems involved, let's get back to the social problems.

QUESTION:

I have only been in Wisconsin for three months, and, therefore, my question does not necessarily apply just to the Green Bay area. We have a problem in Pennsylvania with certain minority groups, groups who have the program entitled the "Ten Year Plan". Those of us who are educated

128

and have been in the hospital field, are quite worried about this. Their idea is that every member of their group should reproduce one child per year for ten years, and then they will attain the power that they desire. I think many of our larger cities do have these minority groups that are in operation, and how do you combat this when you come up with the community hospital clinic problem?

MR. McLAUGHLIN:

I don't think that we have sponsored studies of precisely the kind of group that you are mentioning. I have to say that I am a bit skeptical about how widespread such groups are in this country, or in the world. I might say, just by beginning, however, that in many parts of the world we have encountered groups that believe their political power can only arise from rapid population.

In many societies that, for example, have three or four basic ethnic groups comprising them, there has been initial suspicion at the outset of the family planning program - that the family planning program would be accepted only by one group and that the other groups would all gain in numbers, and when the ethnic groups are matched with political parties divided along ethnic lines, as they are in many countries, then the going gets pretty tough. I think, however, that it's easy to demonstrate from a demographic point of view that in the short run the feasible fertility differences among ethnic, religious, or other groups within a single culture, are not great enough to make any large political difference. In other words, if some groups believe that political power can be achieved by reproducing very quickly - in the process I think guaranteeing themselves a pretty hard life trying to raise so many children - then I think they are simply mistaken. They have misread the demographic facts of life. Really, I think there is nothing to be said about such groups. I think they are misguided, they have misinterpreted the demographic name of the game, they have misread the source of political power in this or any other country, at least in the forseeable future, and I think we must continue to appeal on an individual basis to people whose self interest, I think, is almost always best served by not having tremendous families.

DR. PION:

We are studying non-white militancy and family planning. We study it with the use of "Nationals". By that I mean, a colleague of mine, who is black, Dr. Julius Butler, feels as strongly as I do about everything and is my working colleague. When we go to a black school, I can accompany him; when we go to a white school, he can accompany me. We recruited a black woman, divorced, who just got her Master's degree in population and family planning at the University of Michigan, and I sought after her to come and work in our ghetto area.

I think we should recognize, and not react, and not polarize ourselves to genocide as a concept. Scratch the surface of a couple of population people and you find a bigot. Why not? Scratch the surface of any group of any concerned number of people and you will find anything you look for because we're people - and we have the fallibility of people. We do things for different motivations. Some aspects of population control are genocidal in motivation. Let's recognize that they are. Let's recognize that some people fear the explosion of non-white people around the world; but not only because they are non-white, but because of all of the problems such as substandards of living and the revolutionary kinds of thoughts they will bring. Let's recognize and deal honestly with it.

Let's also, therefore, not direct target population programs in this or any other country because up until now the poor and the non-poor have not recognized population as a problem, the affluent have had numbers of children that will increase the population of the world just as the poor have had. The desired family size amongst the poor and unpoor in America - correct me if I'm wrong Dr. Taeuber - is the difference of one child in the best demographic studies we have. And the best demographic studies we have are ongoing or retrospective. You know - if you have four kids, we ask how many did you want before you started? Ouch! But that's the kind of study we are forced to do very often because how many obstetricians when seeing a new pre-natal patient ask the following question: "What method of birth control were you using when you conceived"? That's the only way you can evaluate a family planning program - not by the numbers of people served in your community. That's what we have to do when we have never had a family planning program before, and justify - you know - a renewal of funding for next year. We have seen 5,000 patients this year. How many patients have you seen in your community who had an accidental pregnancy? The more you have had, the lousier your family program is.

What we have to reverse is the famous poster, somewhat blasphemous, the pointed finger saying "The pill is a no, no", which has widespread distribution on the West Coast. I don't know if it's gotten to Green Bay. Perhaps not. It's a picture of Pope Paul, pointing a finger, saying the pill is a no no. Well, the attitude in family planning must be that it is a yes, yes for everybody. Then we can honestly deal with genocide as a backlash.

DR. KAUFMAN:

My students in discussing population problems regularly point out the physician and the churchman in the community as people who should be leaders in family planning and population regulation. We have seen today something of the interest shown by physicians. I am sure a great many of them are busy and unable to attend. We have also seen, in about an equal number of people, the church. Now, I would like to ask of our churchmen who are here, if they would care to ask a question or comment.

FATHER HOPFENSBERGER:

I hope that wans't a sign of reluctance. I will just address myself a little bit to the coercion problem that came up. It bothers me
a little bit. But I think what we ought to talk about is the principles
that go behind our coercion, not so much in terms of numbers, but also
in terms of quality of people. If we want to talk about coercion from
the government, I don't think it should be in terms of numbers, but in
terms of coercion for education. Because, I have to adjust myself to
abortion tomorrow, because we have to adjust ourselves to abortion,
indicates that there is a problem. To attack the problem, it seems to
me to be education where we educate people to be responsible for their
activity - whether it's in quality, whether it's in numbers, or sexual
activity. We have to talk about responsible activity and people being
responsible for what they do.

FATHER _____:

We should. It's a moral question. I have appreciated very much
the conference and learned a great deal. I was hoping that perhaps
some of the women in the audience would have challenged Dr. Pion on
tubal ligature. If we are to control, I believe we are to control
ourselves. Frequently I have heard mentioned government - self government is a part of our way of life, is it not?

PASTOR OBERT LOWE:

I would just like to ask the question. I think probably there has
already been a lot of discussion, and it seems unanimous about the
seriousness of the matter of population growth, say in our country. I
am wondering if in the process of discussion and talk, this would not
have an effect in itself of changing the trend without going to the
point of making another law with respect to the numbers of children.
And, myself, I feel it would be frightening if we did go into the policy
of using the two figure - that nobody can have more than two children -
simply because there would be families that naturally would be capable
and who ought to contribute these children. And there are others -
other families - where they do not want children. Wouldn't it be far
better to think in terms of making it possible for those who do not
desire children to not have them; and those, on the other hand, who are
able to have a larger number to do so, without having this stigma attached
to having additional children? Is there an overemphasis here? And won't
there be - we have seen in history where there have been cycles? First,
you will have many children in families; and then after a period of time,
then the style is to have fewer children, and won't this even itself out
with just a little discussion on the subject?

DR. PION:

History is a very important consideration, except that we have never had the population problem as acute in history before as we now have it. In this country we have never had the "boob tube" before, as we know it. The words I would like everybody to listen to - they are not my own - they are an advertising man's words who came to work with us one-and one-half years ago, and has been trying to work this problem out. What's he doing with us? My chairman still doesn't understand. His message is not like India's - "stop at two, three's enough". His message is "try for two".

The proposal we have developed is directed to a population of 18 to 28 year olds - males and females - with whatever spinoff that may occur to others. We have chosen that age group, hoping that within the group are people who have not as yet had their third child. They might not have had their first child. The message is "try for two children". We are going to teach them about numbers. We are going to teach them what the demographers want us to know - us - collectively - society! We are going to tell them if they want twelve children, they could adopt ten. What's important - the child or us, or this "genetic mystique" of bad blood? We do a much better job in this country of raising cats and dogs who almost never give us cause to worry about bad blood. We give them food, we give them shelter, and they love us. They grow up loyally. But adoption - and adopting a mixed racial kid - "Oh my God! How are we going to face our neighbors?" That's our concern.

I would like to provide the good Father with some preliminary data for his sermon. The data is unsolicited. These are statistics collected from October 28, 1969 through December 31, 1969. We formally collected them for this conference. Patients referred to our phone counseling service ---- patients referred by Planned Parenthood 31; patients referred by physicians 118; patients referred by friends 13; patients referred by others 54 (many clergymen amongst others). Marital status of the patients: single 136; married 49; divorced 27; separated 4. Age: 12 to 17 year old age group - 40; 18 to 23 - 96; 24 to 29 - 38; 30 and over - 42; the oldest being 51. Religion: Protestant - 135; Catholic - 34; Jewish - 8; None - 37. None means no religious affiliation by background. Other - 2. Schooling: junior high completed - 21, or in junior high; high school completed, or in - 99; 1 to 3 years of college - 68; 4 years of college or more - 28. Weeks pregnant: 1 to 4 weeks pregnant - 19, the overwhelming majority closer to 4 weeks pregnant; 4 to 8 weeks pregnant - 74; 8 to 12 weeks pregnant - 93; 12 to 16 weeks pregnant - 18; over 16 weeks pregnant - 12. The history of whether they did or did not use contraception and why not - and the why not is being cross-correlated now with age. Yes - 55; No - 161. These are 216 patients we are reporting on, all of whom called the office saying "I want an abortion!". Not advertised. When we advertise, I hope come March 1, we will report the statistics and the change in character of patients calling. We only had 5 black women calling out of the 216. We have only had 2 Japanese of the 216.

132

Of the contraceptive users - 55 contraceptive users - 14 were on pills, some of whom said "my doctor discontinued their use because of a problem" - weight gain or something else. "Did the doctor give you some other method?" "No"! IUD - 3, intrauterine devices in place. Diaphragm use - 5. Foam - 15. Condom - 8. Other, including rhythm and no answer - 10. Unmeaningful statistics. Skewed example. People aware of our particular office at our particular University calling in. The State Council of Churches has just, two weeks ago, offered their services to us. We will be getting a different group of patients referred now. We have a Seattle Pastoral Institute that we hope to involve - which is ecumenical - and which does have within it most religions represented. Whether all religions so represented might participate in the counselling service remains to be seen. I wanted to share that with you.

SARAH WATKE:

I would like Dr. Pion, and Dr. Green to comment on this. With regard to your proposed model clinic, what are your Washington laws now? I know that California and North Carolina and some of these other states have liberalized laws, and I am wondering, can states have these consultation clinics without changes in the laws about what you can and can't do for people?

DR. PION:

A simple response. Yes, with medical leadership. Contraceptive prescriptions, sales, display, discussion, is illegal in the State of Washington since 1909 and it's still illegal. All of the counselling we do concerning abortion is illegal. Period!

IRIS FONTERA:

Something has occurred here today which disturbs me. Here we are at a panel and we are all thinking about the danger of the world population and the problems. And we have a gentleman tell us, as friends of mine do, that not only does he have seven children, but he has a four-month old. He's a doctor, he's educated, supposedly he's aware of the problems. If I had a friend who, for example, was playing around in the old sense, I might say to this friend: "How can you do this to your family?" But when we have friends who have too many children we never say - we don't dare say - "how can you do this to the world or to your community?" So it is in a sense, even in this group of supposedly educated, aware people a no - no. None of us responded when this gentleman told us - not only the number of children, that wasn't the thing - but the youngest one. And we just sat here and none of us would want to because it's impolite. Now, how are we going to get this education across that we are talking about?

DR. PION:

By being impolite.

133

DR. COMBS:

This gives me a chance to say something that I don't think has been stated. I agree with Dr. Pion that there is a great potential for education and communication of the problems. But my general observation is that family decisions are made by people with reference to their own local family situation, and the situations in which family size on a national level have been brought down to the replacement level seem to be those in which the social structure carries with it sufficient sanctions (rewards and punishments) with respect to child bearing that a sufficient number of individuals in the society see the reduction in fertility as a rational action from their own personal point of view. This does pose societies with certain problems.

I think we can make some headway in convincing people of the problem, but I doubt very seriously if people make their personal decisions about size of family, that is that most do, in terms of what this is going to do to world population.

I have two daughters. I stopped at two. But I didn't do so because I thought this was my obligation for world population, but because I thought this was my obligation to myself and my children. These were the number that I felt I could educate and meet their other needs according to my value system, as well as my own needs.

There are constraints built in. We all have a certain expectation of salary and we have aspirations we wish to fulfill. But the institutional arrangement of society, I believe, is going to have to be such that it will reward a sufficient number of people for limiting their fertility or punish enough for having too many. I am talking rewards and punishment in the general sense of sanctions, not simply laws - and it will also have a culture which allows people to see that they have a choice on this point. They will be able to perceive that reducing fertility is one of the alternatives open to them, in order to achieve their total aspiration level. We may miss the point, therefore, if we talk too much simply about an educational effort without perceiving that such an effort happens in a social structure that does in one way or another reward people in some aspects and punish them in others.

MR. McLAUGHLIN:

I certainly recognize what Dr. Combs has said about the personal situation, the system of social and economic rewards and punishments that encourage certain family size. I think, however, that when we look at new generations of Americans entering their reproductive years, we assume perhaps not with full reason that they have a very strong preference for the traditional average size of American families of a little over three, as opposed to an average family size of a little over two. We assume that they have, like their forefathers, evaluated their personal, economic situation and their aspirations, and they have said "Yes, it will be 3.2, just as it was for previous generations". I think maybe the preference for a little over three, as opposed to a little over two, may not be as strong as we think it is. It may, in fact, prove vulnerable to just the kinds of appeals to conscience that the lady just mentioned. It may prove for this new generation of Americans that they weren't all that anxious for the third child, and that publicity about the population problems of the world, and even of the United States, may be sufficient to overcome what was, in fact, a rather slight preference.

DR. KAUFMAN:

One question to the panel - to each of the members. In one word, not what is the problem - population is perhaps that word - what is the one key word to the solution?

DR. PION:

Mass communication - I will take more than one word. This is the family planning symbol of India (Dr. Pion held up the symbol - a red inverted equilateral triangle). What if we made it the universal population planning symbol? What if every priest, physician, minister and educator wore it around his neck when he wasn't wearing a tie, and you clergy can wear it all the time? That could become a symbol of morality, and catch on with the young people even more than the peace symbol because population planning might - might - bring peace.

SHARON ESTEL:

I think probably the key word is awareness. There are too many people around here especially that are not aware of this problem. They have been brought up, raised - lots of kids - and they are used to this. And now, I suppose part of it is religious affiliation. They just don't want to think about it; they don't want to become aware. And I think these people have to become aware because it is a problem. About, let's say a year and a half to two years ago, I was one of these people. Well, I had a class this year. I am aware!

DR. GREEN:

Mine is very simple. I believe that we must stop trying to adjust present day things to our old established sense of values. I think we have to adjust our sense of values to present day issues.

DR. COMBS:

I agree with the young lady. I think our problem is to increase awareness at all levels. I am committed to pursuing a program of research and I have to be true to that. I think our primary need is to develop an increasingly broad spectrum of knowledge that will be made available to the general public and to leaders in all walks of life, so that they can make and form decisions to correct the problem.

DR. HARTLEY:

I suppose I will be playing the "heavy" if I say the words I have in mind. They are responsibility and commitment - commitment to the human enterprise. I don't believe we will get very far unless we can also persuade people that no man is an island.

MR. McLAUGHLIN:

Let us develop the public opinion and the political will to exploit the many voluntary approaches that are still open to us.

DR. KAUFMAN:

Ladies and gentlemen, there are about 100 of us here today. You can leave this Symposium as 100 leaders - 1 for every 1000 people in the Green Bay area. Let me turn the microphone to Dean Beaton for the formal adjournment of the session.

ADJOURNMENT

John R. Beaton

At this stage, what can I say? Say that we have enjoyed the talks?
Certainly, we have enjoyed the talks. It's a duty of mine at this point,
and I might add with considerable regret, to bring this two-day Symposium
to a close. I say with regret because this could have gone on much longer.
Hopefully, a year from now we might repeat this, have it last somewhat
longer, certainly have our same speakers, and perhaps others in addition.

I would hope that we could say that the Green Bay situation is not
as pessimistic, let's say, as it might look at the present moment.

Yesterday in my introductory remarks, I stated that one major goal
of this Symposium was to help us at the University develop and implement
our program in instruction, research and community outreach. Certainly,
in the last two days, I think even more this morning, we have heard many
thoughts, many concepts, many ideas, which we should consider very carefully. I think we can develop a meaningful program here, but this is only
a very small part of the total program. Regarded perhaps as the typical
ivory tower, the academic community, we are not theoretically the doers.
I think we can be. I think it's our responsibility.

Perhaps the most important goal of a Symposium such as this is to
begin to promote awareness, as Sherry Estel said, of the serious problems
of overpopulation among our community organizations and its members. I
hope that we have succeeded in this goal. I hope we have enlisted the
aid of our friends in the news media, who, I am very happy to say, responded to this Symposium in significant numbers, representing all forms
of the news media. We can't afford to be complacent and say "it can't
happen here in Green Bay". We have space at the present time. We don't
see great overcrowding. We also know that any demographer, such as Irene
Taeuber, indeed, I think any physician in the community, can tell you it
is happening.

I am not going to go over again, as I did yesterday, the signs and
symptoms we now have. Let me just point out that the rate of population
growth in Brown County is more than double that of the national average
at the present time. I hope action will be forthcoming. This is perhaps
the only significant accomplishment we hope will come out of this Symposium.

As we draw to a conclusion now, I would like to express our most sincere appreciation to all of our invited speakers, certainly to our Panel members of yesterday and this morning, to our colleagues, and I think, most importantly, to our community members representing many organizations or representing nobody, but themselves, and the general community.

A number of our speakers have traveled long distances to be here, taking time from busy schedules. We are especially grateful to them. This certainly indicates their dedication to the solution of population problems. The success of any Symposium depends in a large part upon the participation of our community members. It is upon them that the onus for action now rests. Hopefully, at the University we can provide some leadership, provide a core, a reference, a local bureau if you like, but it is community people that must carry out the action. The community response has been good. Dr. Kaufman said there are about 100 here. I think there are actually about 150 here this morning; we had in excess of 200 yesterday. This is a good response on a subject which in this particular community could be unpopular. I don't think it is, but it could be. We have had response from a number of communities from around Wisconsin, not all in Green Bay. I might add to our benefit and our pleasure, we even had one attendee from Hawaii.

I know I speak on behalf of our organizing committee, Dr. Doberenz, Dr. Taeuber, Dr. Ihrke of our faculty, and Mrs. Jo Berentson when I express our most sincere appreciation to everyone who attended and participated.

Thank you very much for your attendance. I now declare the Symposium adjourned.

SELECTED REFERENCES

Archives of Environmental Health - issue of February 1969 (Vol. 18, No. 2) several articles of interest on pages 235 through 300

American Chemical Society, 1969, Cleaning our Environment, Special Issue Sales, 1155 16th St., N.W., Washington, D.C. 20036

Arguendo: The Legal Challenge of Population Control, 1968, Law and Society Review, Vol. 107.

Bates, Marston, 1965, The Forest and the Sea, Vintage, paperback.

Batten, Louis J., 1966, The Unclean Sky, Doubleday - Anchor

Benarde, M. A., 1970, Our Precarious Habitat, W. W. Norton, paperback.

Carson, Rachel, 1962, Silent Spring, Fawcett Crest.

Commoner, Barry, 1963, Science and Survival, Viking.

Dubos, Rene, 1965, Man Adapting, Yale University Press

Dubos, Rene, So Human An Animal, 1968, Scribner's

Ehrlich, Paul R., 1968, The Population Bomb, Ballantine

Farb, Peter, and the Editors of Life, Ecology, Time, Inc.

Goldman, Marshall I., 1967, Controlling Pollution, The Economics of a Cleaner America, Prentice-Hall, Inc.

Hardin, C. M. (ed), 1969, Overcoming World Hunger, Prentice-Hall, paperback

Hauser, P.M., (ed), 1963, The Population Dilemma, Prentice-Hall, paperback

Laden, L., 1966, Abortion, Beacon.

Leopold, Aldo, 1949, A Sand County Almanac, Oxford University Press

Marx, Wesley, 1967, The Frail Ocean, Ballantine, paperback

Morison, Robert S., Science and Social Attitudes, Science 165, 150-156 (1 July 1969)

New England Journal of Medicine, Vol. 275, 1966 - A series of 10 articles dealing with "man and his environment". They started on the following pages (in different issues) 759, 788, 819, 929, 1100, 1168, 1342, 1413, 1419 and 1478. The series was reprinted by NEJM as a booklet entitled Environmental Hazards.

Novick, Sheldon, 1969, The Careless Atom, Houghton-Mifflin

Odum, Eugene, 1959, Ecology, Holt, Rinehart and Winston.

Osborn, Fairfield, Our Plundered Planet, 1948, Pyramid Book T-1885

Paddock, W. and Paddock, P., 1967, Famine - 1975, Little Brown

Reinow, R. and Reinow, L. T., 1967, Moment in the Sun, Dial, paperback

Sapolsky, Harvey M., Science, Voters, and the Fluoridation Controversy Science 162, 427-433 (25 October 1968)

Shepard, Paul and McKinley, Daniel, 1969, The Subversive Science, Houghton-Mifflin.

Storer, J. H., 1968 Man In The Web of Life, Signet, paperback

Taylor, R. G., 1968, The Biological Time Bomb, World Publishers

Turnbull, Colin M., 1962, The Forest People, Doubleday Anchor

Udall, Stewart L., 1964, The Quiet Crisis, Avon Discus Books NS 24

Vayda, Andrew P., 1969, Environmental and Cultural Behavior, Natural History Press

White, Lynn, Jr., The Historical Roots of Our Ecologic Crisis, Science 155, 1203-1207 (10 March 1967). See also letters to the editor in Science 156, 737-738 (12 May 1967)